A SILVER SAGA

A Silver Saga

VIKING TREASURE
from the NORTH WEST

Fiona A. Philpott
Edited by
James Graham-Campbell

NATIONAL MUSEUMS & GALLERIES
· ON MERSEYSIDE ·

Contents

Foreword

This exhibition has been planned to commemorate the discovery of the hoard of Viking silver treasure found at Cuerdale, Lancashire, 150 years ago. Liverpool Museum holds one of the major collections of coins and bullion from this, the largest hoard of its kind.

The Vikings' use of silver is a theme which features prominently in the exhibition, reflecting its importance within the context of Norse settlement and activity. I hope the exhibition will provide an opportunity to review the significance of the Irish Sea province during the Viking Age.

I would particularly like to thank Dr James Graham-Campbell of University College London, for acting as the academic consultant for the exhibition and Fiona Philpott, Curator of British Antiquities, who has been responsible for organising the exhibition.

An exhibition of this size would not be possible without the support, enthusiasm and assistance of all those who have lent objects in their possession. To them I would like to express my grateful thanks.

Finally, I must thank all those companies who have supported the exhibition, and in particular Pilot Properties who have sponsored this publication.

R. A. Foster

LIST OF SPONSORS

Pilot Properties Limited ● Barclays Bank plc
Birmingham Midshires Building Society ● Charterhouse Tilney

Supported by
Goldsmiths' Company ● Duchy of Lancaster ● Bank of England
Dan Air ● Manx Airlines ● Ryan Air ● Fred Olsen Travel
The Isle of Man Steam Packet Company Limited
Friends of the National Museums & Galleries on Merseyside

Acknowledgements

I would particularly like to thank Dr James Graham-Campbell who has acted as academic consultant for this exhibition and whose comments and advice have been invaluable. My thanks also go to staff and colleagues from universities and museums in Britain, Ireland and Scandinavia who have provided much information and support. I am very grateful to David Griffiths for producing the distribution maps and Mark Blackburn for providing details of mints represented in the Cuerdale hoard. Richard Bailey has most kindly assisted with the selection of sculpture for the exhibition and has commented on the labels. I am grateful to Marion Archibald for selecting coins for the exhibition from the British Museum's collections. Her advice on the text has also been much appreciated.

A project of this size and scale requires the support and commitment of many staff. I am most grateful for the assistance I have received from the following departments; Antiquities, Design and Production, Conservation, Technical Services, Education, Commercial Services and Marketing. In particular I would like to thank Amy de Joia, Rebecca Lang, Helen Thornton, Chris Ryan, Julie Wright, Keith Robinson, Theresa Doyle, Val Evans, Peter Spinks, Bill Sillitoe, Tracey Seddon, Dave Warwick, David Flower, Peter Duncombe, Keith Thompson, Carol Scanlon and Philip Cargill.

Above all, I would like to thank my husband, Robert Philpott, for his constant support, encouragement and professional advice.

Fiona A. Philpott

ONSET
& RAIDS

The Western Isles.

Viking Raiders

*'Behold, the church of St. Cuthbert spattered
with the blood of the priests of God,
despoiled of all its ornaments; a place
more venerable than all in Britain
is given as prey to pagan peoples'*

So wrote the English cleric Alcuin after a devastating Viking attack on the monastery of Lindisfarne, off the coast of Northumbria, in AD 793.

During the closing years of the eighth century pagan Viking raiders swept across the North Sea and into the Irish Sea, attacking defenceless churches and monasteries along the coasts of Scotland, Ireland and England.

In the desire to acquire wealth, precious objects of silver and gold were torn from their mounts; saints' shrines were despoiled; monks, nuns and priests were captured to be sold into slavery or ransomed.

Their success led to more raids, gradually penetrating further inland. Viking longships with their shallow draughts were easily manoeuvred up rivers and inland waterways. Crews leapt onto dry land ready for action, as they brandished their fine weapons at the unsuspecting inhabitants.

Raiding bases were soon established so that ships might be repaired and provisions renewed.

Meanwhile, other warriors from Denmark launched a concerted attack on the Frankish Empire. Towns in France and the Low Countries were sacked and plundered. Fires soon raged across England as the Danish Great Army burnt and pillaged villages, marauding from one winter-camp to another.

By the mid-ninth century the Vikings had brought disruption and destruction to western Europe.

A large amount of metalwork from Britain and Ireland has been found in ninth-century Scandinavian graves. This bronze bowl decorated with enamel was discovered in a man's grave at Myklebustad, Norway.

The Viking Age

These attacks heralded the beginning of the Viking Age which was to last from the ninth to the eleventh century. During this period the Vikings penetrated almost every corner of the then known world. They sailed east into Russia, and beyond to the Caspian Sea, south to the Mediterranean, and west to Britain and Ireland. From here they journeyed north to the Faroes and Iceland, and finally west to Greenland and North America.

They set out from the mountains of Norway, the islands of Denmark and the plateaux and coastal plains of Sweden in search of greater freedom, wealth, land and adventure.

Ships were an essential means of transport around Scandinavia and during the eighth century the Vikings developed light, fast, easily manoeuvrable vessels. These ships made long sea journeys possible and ensured the Vikings' success. Many voyages could have been made within sight of land, but over long distances coastal features, cloud formations, the appearance of sea-birds or whales, and the position of the stars and the sun all helped with navigation.

The Faroe islands rise steeply from the sea limiting the land available for settlement. The Vikings reached the islands by sailing north-west from Shetland, a journey of a couple of days.

THE SCANDINAVIAN HOMELANDS

Norway is very mountainous and settlements concentrate along the coast and at the head of fjords.

The Swedish town of Birka was established c. AD 800 on the island of Björko, in Lake Mälar. It was ideally placed to take advantage of Baltic Sea Trade.

To be a 'Viking', strictly speaking, meant to be a pirate. The majority of Scandinavians were not 'Vikings'. They remained in Norway, Denmark and Sweden, as farmers, fishermen, hunters, trappers, craftsmen and merchants.

Farming practices varied from region to region but, wherever natural resources were good, rich settlements developed.

In general farmers produced what they needed for themselves. They lived in longhouses which sometimes combined living-quarters and a barn under the same roof. Separate buildings might include a storehouse, a smithy and a bath-house. Building styles varied according to the availability of raw materials. Turf and stone houses were built in treeless areas.

Trading Settlements

In Scandinavia, there were a number of important trading centres. Hedeby on the east coast of Viking-age Denmark controlled trade routes from western Europe to the Baltic, whilst Birka on Lake Mälar in central Sweden shipped furs to western Europe and across the Baltic to Russia, Byzantium and the eastern Caliphate. Kaupang situated at the entrance to the Oslo fjord in Norway was probably a seasonal market attracting northern merchants with cargoes of furs, skins, down, walrus ivory and walrus-hide ropes. Each of these settlements operated as a production centre where craftsmen practised ironworking, bone and antler carving, bronze-casting, leatherworking and jewellery manufacture.

Scandinavian merchants became well known in Europe, but the success of trading ventures generated wealth which in turn caused piracy, particularly around the Baltic. An extension of this piracy brought Vikings to western Europe.

Home Life

The Vikings who settled around the shores of the Irish Sea came largely from Norway, with others from Denmark. Weapons, tools, cooking utensils and personal ornaments which had been placed in pagan Viking graves help us to picture their way of life.

Farming tools provide details about methods of cultivation. Fields were tilled with an ard or worked with a hoe and spade, whilst sickles were used to harvest cereals and scythes to cut hay. Barley, oats and rye were the most important crops but wheat, flax for linen and hemp were also grown. Hunting and fishing helped to provide extra food and gravegoods often include spears, arrowheads and knives.

Smith's tools have been recovered from graves. Anvils, hammers and tongs would have been needed on the farm but there were als

Viking merchants used portable balances for weighing out silver.

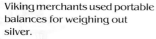

specialist craftsmen using such tools for the production of weapons.

Winter evenings were spent eating and drinking, telling stories and playing games.

Women's Work

Women worked in the fields but also prepared meals and produced clothing and other textiles used on the farm. Food was prepared in iron or soapstone vessels and was cooked over an open fire. Meat was roasted on iron spits, grilled or fried in iron pans. The Vikings had a varied diet which included bread, porridge and many kinds of fish and meat, as well as vegetables, nuts and dairy produce. Clothes were made by spinning and weaving wool and linen. Carding combs, spindle whorls and weaving swords are found in women's graves.

Grave finds often include hunting and fishing implements such as spears, arrowheads, knives, harpoons and fish hooks.

Women were responsible for producing cloth. Combs for carding wool, in preparation for spinning, are sometimes found in graves.

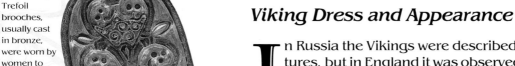

Trefoil brooches, usually cast in bronze, were worn by women to fasten a cloak. This fine silver example comes from Mosnæs, Rogaland, Norway.

Viking Dress and Appearance

In Russia the Vikings were described as the filthiest of God's creatures, but in England it was observed that they combed their hair, bathed and changed so often they were particularly successful in attracting the opposite sex. An Arab merchant, visiting Hedeby in the tenth century, noted that some inhabitants used make-up on their eyes. The number of combs and personal ornaments from Viking graves in Scandinavia tends to suggest that Vikings took pride in their appearance.

Gravegoods can only provide us with a limited amount of information about dress and adornment. Clothing rarely survives, except as small fragments or as impressions on metalwork. The position of brooches, beads and bracelets in graves helps us to draw conclusions about how they were worn, but for further information we can make use of contemporary illustrations.

Women's Clothes

A pair of oval brooches decorated with animal ornament was used to fasten shoulder straps on dresses, with a chemise underneath. A string of beads was often suspended from these or was worn around the neck. Another brooch or pin might be worn on a cape or woollen cloak. Combs, keys and toilet instruments were sometimes suspended from a belt at the waist.

Men's Clothes

Men wore woollen trousers and a shirt under a tunic. Cloaks of wool, sheepskin and fur were tied or fastened with a brooch or pin.

Penannular brooches, fashionable in the Celtic West, became popular both with the Viking settlers and in the homelands.

Fine neck-rings, arm-rings, and finger-rings made from a variety of metals were worn by men, women and children.

Traditional Viking dress.

Viking Silver

Silver was accumulated in vast quantities by the Vikings, and not only through plunder. The majority of silver flowing into Scandinavia will have come through trade. Merchants travelled the great Russian rivers, exchanging furs, honey, weapons and slaves for supplies of Arabic silver coins during the ninth and tenth centuries.

Traditionally, the Scandinavians did not use coins, but operated a bullion economy in which transactions were calculated by weight of silver. Coinage was introduced at the trading settlement of Hedeby, but national coinages were only developed in the late Viking Age.

Coins were melted down in crucibles and cast into ingots. Silver rods, made by hammering out ingots, were twisted or plaited for use

The majority of silver reaching Scandinavia during the ninth and early tenth centuries came from the Arab Empire.

19

as rings. Silver wire was produced and was used for decorating and embellishing weapons. Elaborate brooches, some weighing almost two pounds, were also fashioned from silver.

Ostentatious display was the norm and silver was the visible sign of a successful Viking and his lady. Ibn Fadlan, the Arab chronicler, described women he met in Russia,

> *'Each woman carries on her bosom a container made of iron, silver, copper or gold — its size and substance depending on her man's wealth... Round her neck she wears gold and silver rings.'*

Over one thousand silver and gold hoards have been found in Scandinavia. The Torvik hoard, from Rømsdal in Norway, contains 'Hiberno-Viking' style rings.

Scandinavian Hoards

The earliest silver and gold hoards from Scandinavia contain complete neck-rings, arm-rings and brooches. Some rings conform to a standard size and weight and were probably used as a form of currency. The giving of rings was a traditional way of rewarding followers in Germanic society.

By the tenth century ingots and jewellery were more frequently being cut into pieces to be used as small change. Fragments of silver were weighed out on ingeniously folding scales.

Paganism

The Vikings worshipped several gods. Odin, Thor and Frey were amongst the most popular. Each god had a special area of responsibility. Odin is said to have been the mightiest of all. He was god of war, possessing a spear called Gungnir and an eight-legged horse named Sleipnir. Wolves guarded him and ravens brought him news.

> *'Odin is the highest and the oldest of the gods,*
> *He rules all things, and however powerful*
> *the other gods are they all serve him as*
> *children their father....'*

Thor was Odin's son who protected people against sickness and hunger and was responsible for the growth of crops and for the harvest. He was very much involved with everyday life. He possessed hammer called Mjollnir without which he himself was vulnerable to danger.

Frey was god of fertility who looked after those who were married, whilst his sister Freyja was goddess of love.

Amulets representing the gods themselves or their symbols of power have been found in graves and hoards. Some were made to be worn as pendants whilst others were used for household, burial or votive purposes. Thor's hammer pendants and miniature weapons associated with the cult of Odin seem to have been popular. Crosses also appear in graves from the tenth century illustrating the gradual introduction of Christianity.

Adventures of the Gods

Men, women and children would sit around the fireside listening to their favourite stories and poems about the gods. Many of these were written down by Snorri Sturluson, an Icelandic scholar, in the thirteenth century. They give us a fascinating glimpse into the world of Norse mythology.

One story tells how Odin became the god of all wisdom and patron of poets. The dwarves had made a powerful drink of mead from the blood of a murdered man, Kvasir, who was very wise. Odin stole the drink so that he could make it available to gods and men.

Another tale records Thor's journey to recover his hammer. The giants had stolen it and declared that the hammer would only be returned if Freyja, goddess of love, agreed to marry the giant's lord. Freyja, not surprisingly refused, so Thor decided to trick the giants by dressing up as a bride. Thor found it difficult to behave in a feminine manner and ate a whole ox, a salmon and drank three barrels of mead. When the hammer was brought in to hallow the new bride Thor revealed his true identity and snatched it back.

The end of the world is described by Snorri Sturluson as a great battle between gods and men against giants and monsters. A new world would rise from this evil and destruction. Only two mortals would survive and a few specially chosen gods. The Vikings carved stones depicting such beliefs as on the magnificent Gosforth cross in Cumbria.

This gold foil belongs to a group of sixteen such pieces found in Rogaland, Norway. The scene may represent the god Frey and the giantess Gerd, depicting an old fertility myth in which Frey represents light and Gerd, the earth.

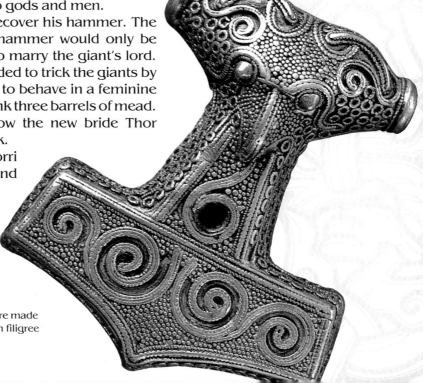

Pendants in the form of hammers, sacred to the god Thor, were made in different metals — the finest of sheet silver, ornamented with filigree and granulation.

Pagan Rituals

Viking burial practice consisted of both cremation and inhumation. Sometimes bodies of the dead were burnt on a funeral pyre and a mound was built over them or the ashes were collected and placed in a pot. Alternatively, the dead were buried in coffins, wagons, wooden chambers or even ships. Graves occur singly or in cemeteries, capped with mounds or cairns or marked with stones, sometimes in the shape of a ship.

This boat burial from Balladoole, Isle of Man, is the grave of one of the island's first Viking inhabitants.

Elaborate ceremonies, including sacrifices, often took place at the funeral of the deceased. The dead were dressed in fine clothes and tools, weapons, furniture and personal ornaments were placed in the grave. It was important that the dead should not return to haunt the living so weapons might be broken or bent. Wagons or ships might have been intended to transport the dead to a new world but may only have served to indicate their wealth and status in society.

Sacrifice

Animals were sacrificed as offerings to the gods and there is considerable evidence to show that human sacrifice could take place as well, as described by Adam of Bremen at Uppsala. Those who volunteered were killed and buried with their masters. Ibn Fadlan, an Arab chronicler, witnessed the funeral of a Viking chieftain in Russia. The man's slaves and wives were asked which of them would be prepared to die. The burial of a warrior from Ballateare, in the Isle of Man, included the body of a woman. The back of her skull had been cut away with a sharp instrument, suggesting that she had been sacrificed.

The most famous ship burials are those from Oseberg and Gokstad, near the Oslo fjord in Norway. The deceased had been buried with ornately carved beds, wagons, sleighs, and chests, together with other household objects. Smaller boat burials have been found in Britain and Iceland. At Kiloran Bay, Colonsay, a warrior was buried in a boat with weapons, tools, a set of scales and weights and his horse. One of the first Viking inhabitants of Man was also buried in a boat, at Balladoole, with his weapons and harness fittings. The grave was then capped with a mound and marked with stones.

The Vikings practised ritual sacrifice as shown by the skull of this young girl, from Ballateare, Isle of Man, which has been sliced away with a sword.

THE
FIRST SETTLERS
OF THE
NORTH WEST

The coast of Harris, Hebrides.

Pagan graves with distinctive tools, weapons and jewellery help us to identify the first Norse settlers of the Irish Sea region. Burials dating to the ninth century have been found in Orkney, Shetland and the Hebrides. Here offshore islands and sea-lochs offered opportunities for fishing, farming and hunting, as well as providing bases from which to launch further raids.

Watercolour plan of the Viking boat burial from Kiloran Bay, Colonsay, Hebrides.

Plan shewing position of various objects found in Viking Grave. Kiloran Bay, Colonsay, and also of Skeleton of Horse.

Skeleton of Horse.

The cemetery of Kilmainham-Islandbridge, outside Dublin, contained numerous graves of well-equipped warriors and their wives.

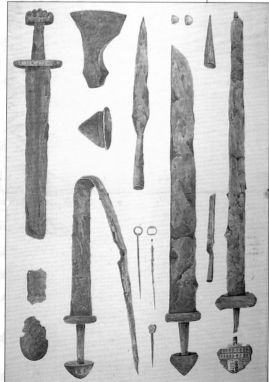

Attacks on Ireland intensified and about AD 841 the Vikings established a permanent base near Dublin, which took the form of a defended fortress. Rich burials from Kilmainham-Islandbridge show that Dublin's first Norse inhabitants included warriors, merchants, craftsmen and their families.

Over forty Viking graves have been discovered in the Isle of Man, most dating to the tenth century. The island appears not to have been gradually settled by family groups, but conquered around AD 900 by Norse warriors who intermarried with the native population.

Meanwhile the Danes invaded England with a huge army and in AD 865 proceeded to conquer Northumbria, East Anglia and most of Mercia during the following years. In AD 867 Halfdan, leader of the Danish Great Army, captured York and installed a puppet-king. Skeletons found in late ninth century levels at Coppergate may have been victims of such a war or civil disturbance. The first kings of York, Ivarr, Halfdan and Sigfrith, also campaigned in Ireland.

Norse-Irish Colonisation of North-West England

The early years of the tenth century saw a separate settlement venture taking place in north-west England by people of Norse-Irish descent. The Vikings were forced out of Dublin by the Irish in AD 902. Some of the refugees may have settled on the Isle of Man; the Irish Annals record that others were given land near Chester, almost certainly on the Wirral. Only a few Viking graves have been found in the north-west of England. With the adoption of Christianity in the tenth century the Vikings buried their dead in churchyards without gravegoods.

The Vikings gave their own names to many of the farms and villages where they settled and used their own terms to describe features of the landscape. These distinctive Scandinavian place-names provide further clues to the areas in which the Vikings lived. Place-names on the Wirral such as West Kirby, Frankby and Raby all contain the Old Norse element 'by' meaning village or farmstead.

The Dee Estuary.

The Story of Ingimund

The Irish Annals preserve an account of the expulsion of a leader called Ingimund from Dublin. Having been forced to leave Ireland, Ingimund and his followers went to Anglesey to seek refuge with King Clydog. Help was not forthcoming so Ingimund and his men sailed on to Cheshire where they were given an audience with Aethelflaed, Lady of the Mercians. She granted them land just outside Chester on which to settle, almost certainly on the Wirral. The profusion of Norse and Norse-Irish place-names on the west side of the peninsula would seem to confirm this view.

Before long Ingimund and his followers saw the wealth of Chester and planned an attack on the city. Aethelflaed was able to prevent this by playing on the divisions which existed between Ingimund's men.

A hoard of 'Hiberno-Viking' type arm-rings found on Anglesey is one of several strands of evidence pointing to Viking settlement and activity along the North Wales coast at this period and may explain why Ingimund and his followers made first for the island. The arm-rings may even have been left behind there by the refugees from Dublin.

The Vikings' Use of Silver in the North West

Raids on Britain, Ireland and the Continent furnished the Vikings with large quantities of silver, part loot and part tribute payments and ransom demands. At the royal capital in York the Danes used their supplies of silver to introduce coinage, inspired by Carolingian issues. The first pennies produced around AD 900 bear the names of the kings Siefred and Cnut.

Meanwhile Vikings active around the Irish Sea region continued to operate a bullion economy. In Ireland the Vikings commissioned elaborate silver cloak pins, based on native Irish designs. They also introduced a new style of arm-ring, now known as the 'Hiberno-Viking' type, consisting of a thick band of silver decorated on the outer surface with stamped ornament. They were made by hammering out standard bar ingots. These together with brooches were chopped up when the need arose and were used as currency, together with fragments of bullion from Scandinavia and the Baltic.

The Earliest Viking-Age Hoards from Britain

Viking silver hoards contain a mixture of coins, ornaments, ingots and cut-up fragments or 'hacksilver'. The discovery of such hoards in Britain and Ireland can help us to trace the movements and activities of the Vikings.

The earliest Viking-age hoards from England and Scotland contain native styles of jewellery and were probably hidden by people fearful of Viking attack.

Pair of Anglo-Saxon silver pins from the Talnotrie hoard

Anglo-Saxon strap-ends from Lilla Howe, North Yorkshire

In contrast, the Croydon hoard from Surrey is clearly Scandinavian in character and is likely to have been buried for safe-keeping by a member of the Danish army which entered London in AD 871-2. Generally, hoards of Scandinavian type concentrate in the north and west of Britain in areas of Norse settlement, for the Danelaw rapidly adopted the use of coinage.

The Vikings who settled in Britain and Ireland were unfamiliar with the use of coins, which they traded as silver bullion. But by the end of the ninth century Viking kings in Northumbria had introduced a series of well regulated silver pennies and halfpennies In so doing they established a monetary economy in which coins of a standard size and weight had a fixed value.

Coins were produced by placing a blank silver flan between two engraved dies. The top die was struck with a heavy hammer to impress the design.

In Ireland, as in Scotland and Wales where there was no existing tradition of using coinage, the Vikings operated a bullion economy. Silver brooches, neck-rings and arm-rings were cut up into fragments and weighed out for small change.

By the beginning of the tenth century there were two separate economic systems on either side of the Irish Sea. One, based on coinage, operated in areas of Danish control, the other, based on bullion, in areas settled primarily by Norsemen.

Elaborate silver cloak brooches were sometimes cut up and the fragments used as bullion.

The Viking warrior, Cnut, became King of York in about AD 900 and soon afterwards began to issue a series of silver pennies bearing his name.

'Hiberno-Viking' arm-rings were produced by Norse settlers in Dublin during the late ninth and early tenth centuries.

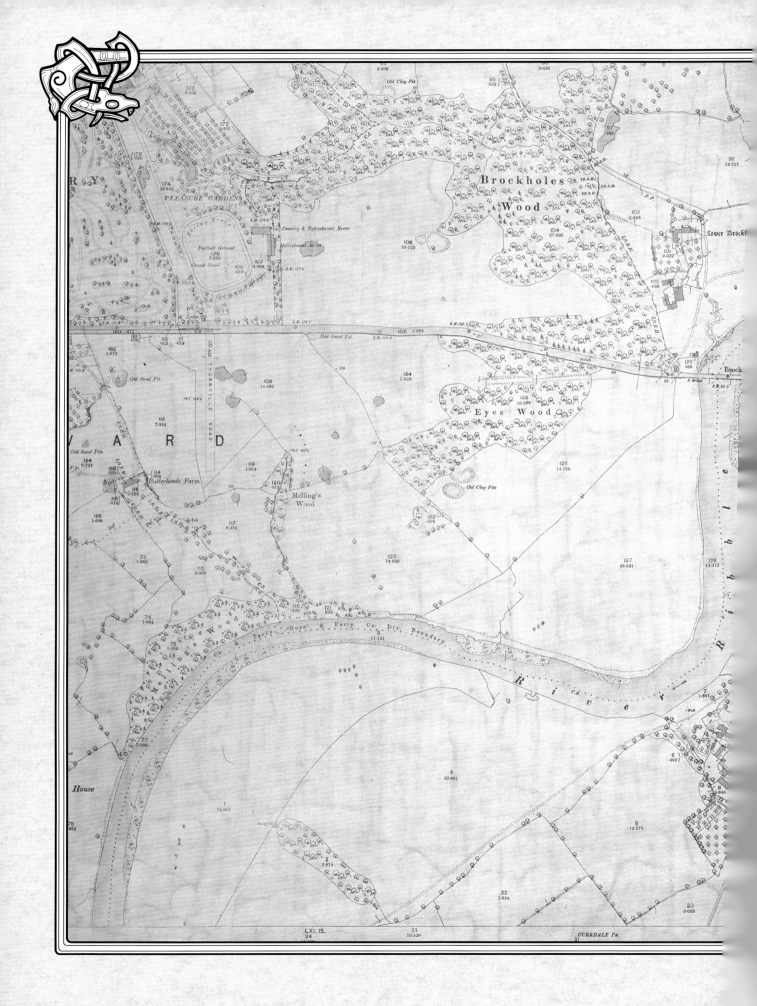

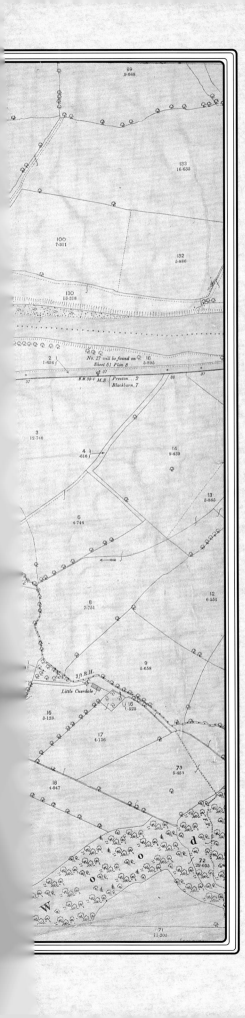

THE DISCOVERY OF THE CUERDALE HOARD

First Edition Ordnance Survey Map of Lancashire.

The Cuerdale Hoard

On 15th May 1840 the largest known hoard of Viking treasure was discovered by workmen as they repaired the embankment of the River Ribble by Cuerdale Hall, near Preston, Lancashire. The hoard, which had been buried in a leaden chest, contained over 8,500 pieces of silver, weighing some 40kg (88lbs).

The Duchy of Lancaster claimed the hoard as treasure trove but William Assheton, the landowner, put in a counter-claim. An inquest was held at the Bull Inn, Preston on 15th August 1840 to decide ownership.

The jury declared the hoard to be treasure trove and so the property of the Duchy. The British Museum was allowed to study the find in great detail and afterwards the Duchy of Lancaster distributed it to over 170 private collectors and public institutions.

The Discovery

William Assheton's workmen had been busy on the river-bank for several weeks when Thomas Marsden suddenly hit something hard with his spade. Thinking it was lime or cockleshells he did not pay too much attention until James Walne threw some soil into his wheelbarrow. Suddenly he realised they had unearthed silver coins.

The shouts of excitement attracted the attention of Jonathan Richardson, Mr Assheton's bailiff. He immediately ordered the men to take the silver to Cuerdale Hall, thinking the treasure belonged by right to Mr Assheton, the owner of the land. Richardson allowed each workman to keep a single coin but the temptation to hide a few extra pieces must have been great. One of the men is said to have carried off more than twenty coins in his boots.

At the Hall the silver was placed in a tub of water and washed with a birch broom and the following day a wooden box was made for it. The treasure was then taken to the bank of Messrs Pedder Fleetwood and Pedder in Preston to await the return of William Assheton who was then in Italy.

The hoard was buried near the bank of the River Ribble at a point where the river might be easily crossed.

The Treasure Trove Inquest

News of the discovery spread quickly and within a week the Duchy of Lancaster had put forward a claim of treasure trove. The case for the Duchy was prepared by their solicitor Mr Teesdale whilst Mr Addison acted for William Assheton. The Duchy's case rested on a statute of King Henry I which stated that objects of silver or gold deliberately hidden and not recovered should become the property of the Crown. If accidentally lost they would become the possession of the landowner. This law of treasure trove still stands.

The inquest was eventually held at the Bull Inn, Preston, on 15th August 1840, exactly three months after the discovery. The jury which consisted of local tradesmen and gentlemen spent the first day examining the findspot. They had to determine whether the hoard had been deliberately concealed or accidentally lost.

The jury eventually declared the hoard to be treasure trove and so the property of the Duchy.

The Dispersal of the Hoard

Queen Victoria kindly gave permission for the British Museum to be presented with a major selection of material from the hoard. A number of coins were also chosen for Queen Victoria's own private collection. The remaining silver was to be distributed by the Duchy of Lancaster. For almost five years the

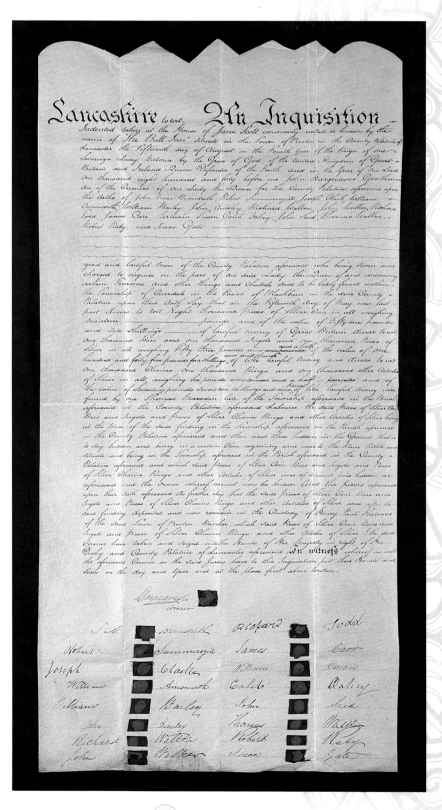

An official statement of the enquiry was witnessed by the jury.

the Duchy was besieged with requests from Britain, Ireland, France, Germany and Denmark. The distribution of the hoard was organised by Dawes Danvers, Clerk of Council. One of the largest groups of coins went to Mr Cuff of the Bank of England, a well-known individual.

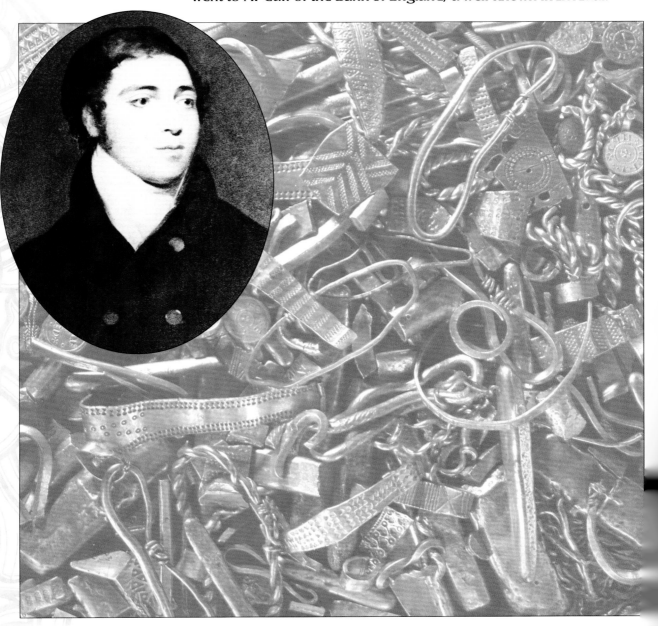

William Assheton owned the land on which the Cuerdale hoard was found.

William Assheton was rewarded with a gold coronation medal and duplicate coins and bullion from the hoard, in a fine rosewood cabinet. His bailiff Jonathan Richardson was given twenty pounds plus a silver coronation medal. William Assheton later gave Richardson pieces from his own collection.

The Nelson Collection of Cuerdale Material

A hundred years after the hoard's discovery Philip Nelson, a doctor and a distinguished coin collector from Liverpool began purchasing Cuerdale material from salerooms and private collectors.

Nelson acquired many coins and over forty pieces of bullion with a Cuerdale provenance, but a few of these pieces have since been shown to have come from other sources, including Oxfordshire, Ireland and possibly even India.

Part of his collection, now in Liverpool Museum, originally belonged to Jonathan Richardson, Assheton's bailiff. The history of some pieces, however, will now never be traced.

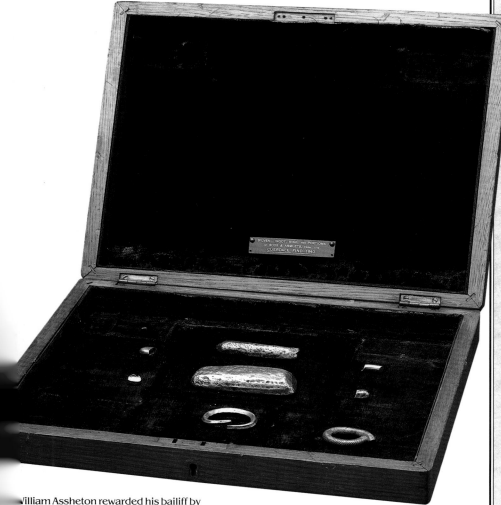

William Assheton rewarded his bailiff by giving him a selection of ingots and ornaments from his own collection of Cuerdale material. These now belong to Liverpool Museum.

THE
CUERDALE
HOARD

The Cuerdale hoard is exceptional not only for its size but also for the number and variety of its contents.

The Contents of the Cuerdale Hoard

The Cuerdale hoard is remarkable not only for its size but also for the number and variety of its contents. It is calculated that it contained about 7,500 coins and 1,000 ingots, ornaments and cut fragments of silver, gathered together from across the Viking world. Coins from the Middle East, bullion from Ireland and loot from the Continent were amongst the silver hidden in the bank of the Ribble.

The treasure was buried in a lead-lined chest, the decayed remains of which were also discovered. Five bone pins thought to have come from Cuerdale may have sealed money bags containing the coins. Despite the large amount of cut up silver, there are very few pieces of waste or manufacturing debris and very few complete objects (with the exception of the ingots). The hoard is therefore unlikely to have belonged to a silversmith.

The Vikings were very concerned about the quality of silver and frequently tested both bullion and coins by pecking the surface or nicking the edge.

Ingots, coins and ornaments from the Cuerdale hoard purchased by Philip Nelson.

38

The Dating of the Cuerdale Hoard

Coin hoards are one of the most important sources of evidence for the Viking period. Coins are particularly useful because they bear inscriptions telling us where and by whom they were produced.

Hoards also provide information about the types of coins in general circulation at any one time and in mixed hoards help to date associated ornaments and decorative metalwork.

By working out which coins were the last to be added to a hoard and by noting the amount of wear they show it is possible to establish the date of burial. A more accurate date can be given by identifying those coins which are absent but which appear in hoards of a slightly later date.

The latest coin from the Cuerdale hoard bearing an actual date is an Abbasid dirhem (Arabic coin) of AD 895-6, which also has a freshly minted appearance. This is not the most recent coin in the whole hoard, however, as there are over 55 coins of Edward the Elder who did not succeed to the Wessex throne until AD 899. Another clue to the puzzle is provided by the badly damaged fragment of a papal coin of King Louis III and Pope Benedict IV which dates to AD 901-3. There are also coins of Louis the Blind, Emperor of the West Franks, which date between AD 901-5.

Later issues of Edward the Elder are not present in the hoard. Also absent are coins of Berengar of Italy as Emperor after AD 915 and the St. Peter series of coins struck at York and those of Regnald, King of York, from around 920.

All these strands of evidence combine to suggest that the Cuerdale hoard was buried about AD 905.

Silver Ingots

Ingots provided a practical means of storing large amounts of silver and could be easily halved, quartered or sliced into required amounts. They were made by pouring molten metal into stone or clay moulds and could have been produced anywhere in the Viking world. Tiny droplet ingots were made when there was too little silver to fill a mould.

The Cuerdale hoard contained over 350 ingots and ingot fragments of varying shapes and sizes. There is a unique group cast to a standard weight and size, some marked with a cross.

By weight, ingots formed the largest component of the Cuerdale hoard.

They are larger and heavier than other ingots in the hoard. Their weight corresponds closely to the mark, a unit of weight used by the Anglo-Saxons for accounting purposes, equal to 160 silver pennies.

The Church of Hagia Sophia, Istanbul. Here, in the gallery, Vikings scratched their names in runes.

Silver from across the Baltic and the North Sea

Scandinavians were drawn to Russia, trading slaves, amber, walrus and furs for silks and spices from Byzantium and China but above all for silver coins of the Arab Empire. The Cuerdale hoard contained fifty Arabic coins from mints as far afield as Afghanistan and Spain, almost certainly obtained from merchants in the Baltic, together with locally made arm-rings and brooches.

Viking merchants also acquired silver neck-rings from Russia. In Scandinavia such neck-rings were twisted into arm-rings; in Denmark this fashion was copied. These rings like all the others might later be cut up and used as bullion, as shown by the forty fragments from the Cuerdale hoard.

Denmark itself was certainly the source of four coins from the hoard and of pieces from arm-rings. In Norway trefoil-headed pins were fashionable and there are a few fragments of these from Cuerdale.

Arabic and Baltic material is rarely found in Viking-age hoards from England but is more common in Ireland, so that part of the treasure may well have reached north-west England via the Irish Sea. The only Byzantine coin from the hoard, already an heirloom when buried, may also have travelled the same route.

Scandinavian Silver Ornaments

The small number of complete twisted and plaited arm-rings and neck-rings from the hoard, together with their many fragments, could have come from almost anywhere in the Viking world. It is impossible to say how these standard fashionable types of personal ornament reached the north-west of England. The same is true of the massive rod arm-rings, cast bracelets, finger-rings, beads and chains included with the treasure.

An amulet in the form of a hammer sacred to the god Thor is one of the most distinctive Scandinavian ornaments from the hoard.

British and Continental Silver

Pictish silversmiths may have made two objects in the hoard. The unique comb fragment and a silver strip with interlace ornament were probably obtained through Viking activity in the Orkneys.

Late ninth-century Anglo-Saxon England had mints in Mercia and Wessex producing a fine series of silver pennies. There are over a thousand of these in the Cuerdale hoard, most issued during the reigns of King Alfred and his successor, Edward the Elder. It is striking that the hoard contained only three or four small pieces of Anglo-Saxon decorative metalwork in comparison with the large number of coins.

Viking raids on France in the 890s and on the Netherlands in AD 902 yielded Frankish and Italian coins, over a thousand of which were buried with the Cuerdale hoard. Three or four pieces of Carolingian metalwork from France, re-used as ornaments, will have come ultimately from the same source.

The Vikings of Northumbria began producing coins just before AD 900. The hoard contained some 5,000 Viking silver pennies mostly issued by the Danish rulers Siefred and Cnut at York. The mint condition of many of them shows that they had only just been added to the treasure.

Native Irish and Hiberno-Viking Silver

Ireland was the source for much of the bullion. The hoard contained over forty fragments of native Irish brooches which must once have adorned the cloaks of both Irish and Viking warriors and merchants. Three or four fragments are from brooches made by Viking craftsmen, copying these native Irish fashions.

There are also large numbers of arm-rings of types once popular with Viking settlers in Ireland. Complete pieces showing few signs of wear must have been added to the treasure just before it was hidden.

Even though the Danish inhabitants of York had begun minting coins at the close of the ninth century, the Norsemen from Ireland still used bullion as a form of currency. As a result there are no Irish-Viking coins from the hoard.

'Thistle' brooches originated in Ireland during the second half of the ninth century.

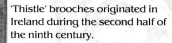

41

Who Buried the Hoard and Why?

Vikings buried hoards of treasure for safe-keeping, particularly in times of trouble or before setting off on long journeys. They were often hidden close to landmarks, by trees, or riverbanks so that they could be recovered easily.

Exactly who buried the Cuerdale hoard and why it was never recovered will always remain a mystery. One theory is that the Ribble estuary was being used as a powerbase from which to reassert Norse control across the Irish Sea.

After being expelled from Dublin in AD 902 some Vikings and their Irish followers began to settle along the north-west coast of England. The large amount of Irish bullion from the hoard may have been brought to Lancashire at this time.

The huge quantity of coins from York was possibly supplied by Danish supporters keen to assist in a renewed campaign against Ireland. In modern values the hoard is thought to have been worth approximately £300,000, sufficient to raise a fleet and pay a band of warriors.

The hoard was too heavy to have been carried and hidden by one man. Failure to recover the treasure suggests that disaster befell its owner or owners and all those involved in its burial!

Hoards of silver and gold were buried for safekeeping.

Viking Coins in the Hoard

Coins from the Cuerdale hoard recall the dramatic political events of the late ninth century when the Danish Great Army fought its way through England.

Viking warriors attacked East Anglia in AD 869, murdering King Edmund. When peace was restored, the Viking leader Guthrum was baptised as a Christian king. He issued a series of coins bearing strong similarities to pennies of King Alfred of Wessex. The letters on the obverse legend are divided into four groups. At the end of the ninth century a coinage was struck in memory of St. Edmund, which continued in production for a short time after 905.

Halfdan, commander of the Danish army, captured London in about 872. Silver pennies bearing a London Monogram, issued in the name Halfdan may possibly be associated with the very same Danish warrior.

The Cuerdale hoard contained 3,000 coins bearing the names Cnut and Siefred, two of the earliest Viking kings of York. Siefred fought in Northumbria in 893/4 and became king of York c. 895. Cnut is associated with a king of the same name mentioned in Viking sagas as campaigning in Northumbria c. 900. The two kings may have shared the kingdom for a period as both names appear on some coins. The designs and legends of their coins bear strong Christian and Frankish influences.

Anglo-Saxon Coins

Despite the Viking attacks, Wessex and Kent remained in Anglo-Saxon hands and during King Alfred's reign (871-99) mints were opened at London, Oxford (Osnaforda), Gloucester, Exeter and Winchester, in part reflecting the gradual expansion of Alfred's kingdom into Mercia. Most of his coin designs were borrowed and copied by the Vikings.

A new reverse coin design was introduced by King Alfred bearing two emperors seated with a Victory above. This design was copied from Roman coins and may have been intended to commemorate an alliance between Wessex and Mercia against the Danes. A silver penny bearing the king's portrait and a large monogram of London on the reverse was struck to celebrate Alfred's capture of London from the Vikings.

The largest issue of Alfred's reign consisted of pennies and halfpennies with the King's title in a continuous arrangement on the obverse and with the moneyer's name in two lines on the reverse divided by pellets or crosses.

King Alfred was succeeded by Edward the Elder in 899. Only his earliest issues are present in the hoard. Some coins bearing the letters BATH across the reverse indicate that a new mint was opened up at Bath.

Silver penny of Alfred, King of Wessex 871-99. This is one of the coins found with the Cuerdale hoard.

Silver denaro of Berengar I of Italy.

The Archbishops of Canterbury struck their own series of coins, modelled closely on issues of the kings of Wessex and Mercia. Plegmund, 890-923, whose coins also appear in the Cuerdale hoard, was the last Archbishop of Canterbury to strike coins in his own name.

Frankish and Italian Coins

The Cuerdale hoard contained about a thousand Frankish and Italian coins. Both regions formed part of the Carolingian Empire which included all western Europe except the British Isles and most of Spain. It takes its name from Charlemagne or Charles the Great, 768-814, its greatest ruler.

Charlemagne and his father Pepin brought coinage under state control, restoring the weight and purity of coins. Gradually the Empire was divided up amongst Charlemagne's heirs, all of whom issued silver deniers or obols (halfpennies). There were two main types of coins: the Temple type which had a cross and pellets on the obverse and a temple on the reverse, and the Christiana religio type. A separate series of denari was struck in Italy from 855 onwards, all of the Temple type. Coins issued by the Pope also had to bear the Emperor's name, as illustrated by the coin of Louis III and Pope Benedict IV from the hoard.

Coins in the name of Charles the Bald, King of France, 840-877, but most probably issued later, are well represented in the hoard. Issues of his sons are also included. A large number of Frankish coins from the hoard were produced at the mints of Melle, Limoges and Le Mans. Melle was situated close to silver mines in Aquitaine. Coins from the important commercial centres of Quentovic and Dorestad are also present.

Italy was ruled, amongst others, by Charles the Bald of France, 875-7, Carloman of Bavaria, 877-9, Charles the Fat of Germany, 879-87, and Louis III of Provence, 900-905, all of whom issued coins which appear in the Cuerdale hoard.

Scandinavian merchants travelled to Russia with furs and slaves to bring back Arabic coins.

Arabic Coins

After the death of Mohammed in the seventh century, the Arab Empire grew rapidly. By the eighth century it extended as far as Spain, North Africa and the eastern Mediterranean, including the Asiatic coast of Turkey.

The first dynasty was descended from a man called Umaiya. It was one of the Umayyad Caliphs, Abd-al-Malik, AD 685-705, who introduced silver dirhems. The Cuerdale hoard included about fifty such coins and fragments, ranging in date from 772 to 895/6. The largest group of coins from the hoard belongs to the Abassid Caliphs who overthrew the Umayyads during the eighth century, although one member of the Umayyad family escaped and set up a new dynasty at Cordova in Spain. The Cuerdale hoard contained only one Umayyad coin, struck at Al-Andalus in AD 869-70.

The Arab mints represented in the hoard range from Cordova in Spain to the Hindu Kush mountains in Afghanistan. The hoard contained a number of Armenian imitations of Arab coins and for this reason it has been suggested that the coins followed a route from Baghdad, via Armenia, into Russia where they were obtained by the Vikings.

Hoards containing coins, ingots, ornaments and hacksilver concentrate in areas of Norse settlement.

Contemporary Viking-Age Hoards

The Cuerdale hoard and others from around the Irish Sea illustrate the wealth in the hands of Viking warriors, pirates and merchants. Supplies of Arabic coins and arm-rings from the Baltic continued to circulate in the early tenth century, often as fragments to be used as small change alongside much else.

A dozen hoards containing a related range of coins and bullion to Cuerdale have been found in northern England, Wales and Ireland. But they are very much smaller and thus highlight the extraordinary size of the Cuerdale hoard.

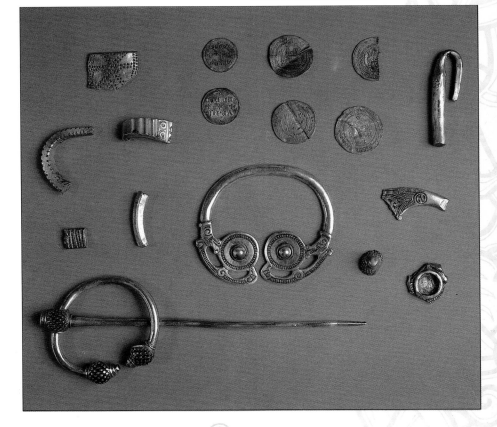

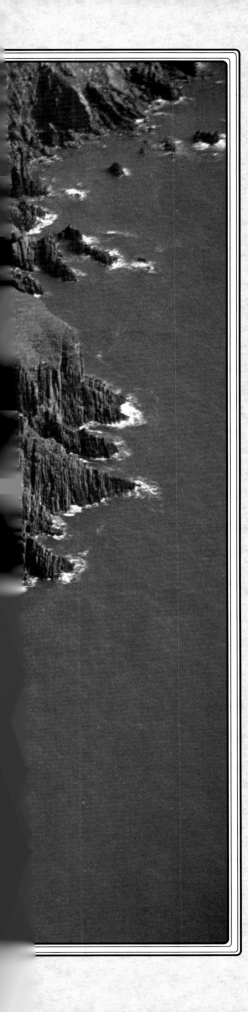

THE IRISH SEA PROVINCE & BEYOND

The coast near Whithorn, Galloway.

Settlements of the Irish Sea Province

Place-names of Norse or Danish origin enable us to identify areas in which the Vikings lived, even though few traces of these settlements survive. Excavation has revealed flourishing urban centres at York in northern England and Dublin in Ireland. In other areas Vikings took over farmsteads and estates or established new settlements, adapting themselves to the local landscape. Opportunities for trade were seized and small coastal settlements evolved which could take advantage of passing merchant ships, as at Whithorn in Galloway, Scotland.

Scandinavian merchants brought international trade to the Irish Sea. From the Baltic came amber, and silks from the Far East. Craftsmen introduced Scandinavian art-styles. Exquisite carvings and metalwork survive displaying Borre, Jellinge, Mammen, Ringerike and Urnes designs. It was a time of great prosperity.

Close links existed between the Norse communities of the Irish Sea. Objects were traded between them and ideas were shared. In all areas the new settlers absorbed the tastes and fashions of the native inhabitants. The Vikings were converted to Christianity and began commissioning stone monuments in memory of their dead. These crosses and grave slabs combine Celtic, Anglian and Scandinavian traditions.

Politically, life remained unpredictable. All Norwegian areas were claimed by the King of Norway but in essence they were ruled by chieftains squabbling for control. The Norse re-established themselves in Ireland in AD 917 and a few years later a Norwegian warrior, Ragnald King of Dublin, seized the throne at York. His successors had to contend with attempts to bring the city under English control, which was only achieved on the death of Eric Bloodaxe in AD 954.

York

York was seized from the Anglo-Saxons in AD 867 and became the capital of a Viking kingdom. The city was already a busy market town but the Vikings extended long distance trading contacts so that by the year AD 1000 York is said to have been 'filled with the treasures of merchants, chiefly of the Danish race'.

Ships laden with silks from the East, pottery from Northern Syria, amber from the Baltic, soapstone from Norway and lava quern-stone from the Rhineland sailed up the Ouse to the quaysides.

The town, situated between the River Ouse and the River Foss, had a busy industrial and commercial quarter. Excavations by the York Archaeological Trust have revealed tradesmen's workshops with evidence for metalworking, woodturning, shoemaking and repairing, beadmaking, bone and antler working as well as carving in wood and stone.

Excavations at Coppergate, York.

Merchants and craftsmen lived in small houses made from wattle and daub or timber, which opened onto the street, with workshops behind. As in Dublin individual plots were separated by fences. The royal palace has not yet been found but it is thought to have been close to York Minster.

The city had a strong Christian tradition which soon influenced the Danish settlers many of whom were converted to Christianity at an early date. Tenth-century burials from the Church of St. Mary Bishophill Junior show a mixed pagan and Christian population.

The York mint started to produce silver coins vital for international commerce. An ecclesiastical series was issued during the tenth century in the name of St. Peter, bearing a sword and hammer on the reverse.

Structures, finds and other information uncovered during excavations at Coppergate have enabled the York Archaeological Trust to reconstruct life in tenth-century York.

Dublin

The Vikings re-established a trading base at Dublin in AD 917. Before long it became the centre of Norse power in the West, well situated to take advantage of a network of trade routes. Merchants sailed from Dublin to markets in the Baltic, Scandinavia, Iceland, England, France and Spain.

The town supported many craftsmen producing both household objects and luxury goods. The products of metalworkers, including the bones on which they sketched their patterns, are well represented amongst the finds. Artists combined Viking, native and insular designs to create styles unique to Dublin.

Waterlogged levels from the Viking period have helped to preserve many organic artefacts such as leather bags and shoes, wooden pails and boxes as well as highly ornate, painted carvings.

Excavations have revealed over two hundred small and crowded wattle houses, built in successive layers on individual plots of land. The town had its own defences consisting of an earthen rampart which was later replaced by stone.

Dublin was the most successful Viking town in Ireland but ports were also established at Limerick, Cork, Wexford and Waterford. Fierce opposition from the Irish restricted Norse settlement to the coast. The Vikings remained in Ireland but after the battle of Tara in AD 980 their kings paid tribute to Irish overlords.

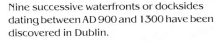

Nine successive waterfronts or docksides dating between AD 900 and 1300 have been discovered in Dublin.

Crafts

Towns rich in supplies of raw materials attracted craftsmen, who would find a ready market for their products amongst wealthy merchants and traders. Leatherworkers, jewellers and beadmakers, blacksmiths and woodworkers would congregate in different streets.

Amber imported from the Baltic was used for making pendants, beads and gaming pieces. It was valued not only as an ornament but also for the magical properties it was thought to possess. Jewellery was also fashioned from jet. The raw material could only be obtained from Whitby on the Yorkshire coast and must have been one of York's chief exports.

Combmakers were found in many centres, manufacturing combs from red deer antler. Long plates were made to form the comb back and between these was riveted a series of rectangular plates into which teeth were cut. Comb cases were carved from strips of antler so that combs could be suspended from the waist without being damaged. Both were often decorated with punched designs, incised lines and sometimes runes.

Bronze casting was carried out in all Scandinavian markets. Metalworkers also made silver and gold jewellery or mass produced ornaments in cheaper metals.

Wooden bowls, platters and buckets were made at market centres alongside some of the finest pieces of carving imaginable. Decorative finials, once painted, were made to adorn buildings and embellish pieces of furniture.

Art-Styles

Animal designs formed the basis for Scandinavian art, bringing excitement and colour to the Vikings' lives. Almost every item was decorated, from the smallest harness fitting to massive stone monuments, providing craftsmen with a wide range of material on which to express their artistic skills.

The first of the Scandinavian styles of Viking art to become established in the British Isles is known as the Borre style. The principal element of this art style, to become popular in the Isle of Man and northern England, a ring-cha

Shoes were made from goat-skin and cow-hide.

The Vikings produced exquisite carvings in wood. This decorated finial was found during excavations in Dublin.

interlace design. The Jellinge style is characterised by ribbon shaped animals seen in profile. The Borre and Jellinge styles were contemporary for a while but in Britain during the tenth century the Jellinge style was preferred.

The Mammen art style grew out of Jellinge designs and it can be difficult to distinguish between them. In general the animal's body becomes more naturalistic, the hip joint is increased in size and patterns on the animal's body become more intricate. Elaborate foliage designs based on vine scrolls and acanthus leaves were introduced with this art-style from the mid-tenth century.

The Ringerike style developed from Mammen designs by the eleventh century. Foliate patterns became the principal element of this new art form, but animals remained popular.

The Urnes style represents the last phase of Viking art. Curving bodies of animals are gracefully intertwined, tapering or swelling as the design dictates. A version of it was particularly popular in Ireland during the late eleventh and early twelfth centuries.

Isle of Man

The Isle of Man, rich in agricultural land, attracted Norse warrior-merchant-farmers, the first of whom were buried (as pagans) beneath large mounds. Excavations have identified a Norse farmstead at the Braaid, Marown. It consisted of a large bow-sided hall built of earth and stone, and a byre or barn. The buildings were found close to the remains of a circular house of native type. Settlement was dense and it became necessary to work marginal land. A hill-farm, excavated at Doarlish Cashen, Patrick, had a corn-drying kiln showing that arable farming was practised there.

St. Patrick's Isle, controlling the only sheltered harbour on the west coast of the island, developed into a major ecclesiastical centre as the seat of the Bishops of Sodor and Man, whose diocese embraced the Western Isles of Scotland. The Kingdom of Man and the Isles was firmly established by Godred Crovan at the battle of Skyhill in AD 1079.

No signs of manufacturing or commercial activity (other than a coin hoard) have yet been found on St. Patrick's Isle but a number of Norse graves were discovered during excavations from 1982-4, together with a mid-eleventh century building. The cemetery included one of the richest female burials found in the British Isles. This grave contained household objects such as a spit, knives and needles, as well as a magnificent necklace of glass beads.

The Norse settlers governed their island through the Tynwald or General Assembly. This early form of democratic government survives to this day, with an annual open-air assembly. Each year on the fifth of July crowds gather around Tynwald Hill to hear the new laws proclaimed in Manx and English.

The Urnes style takes its name from the woodcarving at the small church of Urnes in Western Norway.

St. Patrick's Isle, Peel, Isle of Man.

Chester and Meols

The church dedicated to the Norwegian king St Olaf, stands in Lower Bridge Street, Chester.

Chester was a flourishing Anglo-Saxon market town with a large merchant population. Excavations have provided evidence for the existence of a Viking community just outside the city walls in the region of Lower Bridge Street. Timbered buildings similar to houses in York and Dublin have been found in association with Viking artefacts. During the eleventh century there was a tanning industry in this part of the city which may have been operated by Viking craftsmen. Moneyers bearing the names Oslac, Thurstan and Irfara ('the Ireland journeyer'), worked at the Chester mint. A church which still survives in Lower Bridge Street was dedicated to St. Olave, the Norwegian king Olaf killed in AD 1030.

The city has produced a large Viking hoard containing over five hundred pieces of silver buried in a pot c. 965 — coins, ingots, ornaments and hacksilver — drawn from both the Irish Sea region and

Anglo-Saxon England. Contact with Ireland was particularly strong and both coins and pottery were exported from Chester to Dublin and other coastal ports.

Meols, near the mouth of the Dee Estuary, was once a thriving trading place. Its name is derived from the Old Norse word for sandbank, 'melr'. Ringed pins and other metalwork finds from the site demonstrate that Viking merchants exchanged goods there.

Whithorn, Galloway

At Whithorn in south-west Scotland the Norsemen established a trading and manufacturing centre, close to the site of a Christian community. Excavations since 1986 have revealed workshops and signs of industrial activity. Thousands of off-cuts, boots and shoes provide evidence of leather-working. A number of cat skulls have been found on the site indicating that cat-skins were being used, possibly as fur trimmings for hats. Antler tines, unfinished comb plates and completed pieces suggest the presence of a combmaker's workshop. At a later period ironworking was practised. Hones were probably used for sharpening and finishing tools, whilst handles were produced from red deer antler. A distinctive form of pottery, similar to York ware, has been discovered but there is no clear indication where this was produced.

The Norse must have settled at Whithorn through negotiation with the native aristocracy who granted trading rights in return for the luxuries and commodities of the Scandinavian world.

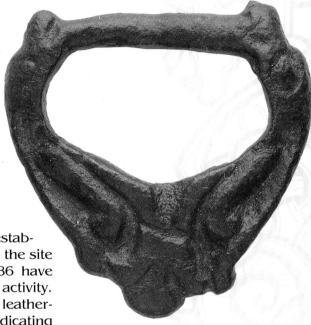

Bronze buckle found at Meols, Wirral.

At Whithorn the Norsemen used wattle and turf for the construction of simple rectangular buildings.

Aerial view of excavations at Whithorn, Galloway.

The Udal, North Uist

xcavations at the Udal suggest that the Vikings settled here in the mid-ninth century, totally obliterating the native inhabitants. Viking rectangular longhouses made of stone and turf overlie native curvilinear buildings. There is a small fort with massive stone walls which may have been built by the Picts as defence against the Norse invaders.

The Norse community at the Udal consisted of farmers and fishermen. Shell sand supported a lush vegetation and the site provided good access to the sea and passing trade. Families would have been self sufficient, producing enough food, clothing and utensils for their own needs. One of the most exciting discoveries from the site has been the identification of a coarse type of pottery which was pressed out into baking slabs, which has since enabled other Norse settlements in the Western Isles to be recognised. Fragments of metalwork and a coin of Harald Hardrada point to the settlement's continuing contacts with Norway as late as the eleventh century.

Bone pins, used for fastening cloaks, were carved in a variety of shapes and sizes, as these examples from the Udal in the Hebrides show.

Polished stone spindle-whorls and hones from the Viking-age farmstead at Bryant's Gill, Kentmere, Cumbria.

Rural Settlement in North-West England

Intensive survey projects in the North West have located two upland sites dating to the Viking period at Ribblehead in Yorkshire and Bryant's Gill in Cumbria.

A farmstead consisting of three buildings grouped around a courtyard was found at Ribblehead. These appeared to be associated with a field system covering several hectares. Finds from the site point to a mixture of craft and agricultural activities. The stone quern would have been used to grind corn grown on the farm. Coins discovered in the main building suggest that the site was being used during the ninth century.

At Bryant's Gill, situated 290 metres up in the north-western fells of Kentmere, the remains of a large building have been found, measuring approximately 10 metres by 5 metres. The site itself was located at the centre of a 20 hectare field system. Finds from the building include charcoal, iron slag, spindle whorls and a broken whetstone which would originally have been used for sharpening tools and knives. Elsewhere on the site lathe-turned shale spindle whorls, over twenty whetstones or hones and iron artefacts, including horseshoe fragments and an auger for boring holes, have been found. The occupants of the farmstead appear to have been spinning cloth and producing sufficient ironwork for their needs.

We are unable to determine the cultural identity of the inhabitants of these two settlements. The artefacts which survive are not distinctively Scandinavian but the farmsteads belonging to Viking colonists of north-west England were probably very similar in layout and operation to those from Ribblehead and Bryant's Gill.

Late Viking-Age Silver and Gold Hoards and Ornaments

Silver and gold hoards show that there was a marked increase in the amount of silver in circulation during the tenth century. Dublin became particularly rich through its involvement with international trade. Large numbers of Anglo-Saxon coins from the Chester mint found in Ireland point to strong commercial links with northern England.

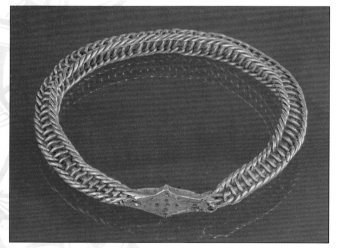

Plaited gold arm-ring from Virginia, Ireland.

Towards the close of the century the Vikings in Dublin started to strike their own coins. Some of these copied Anglo-Saxon pennies, even using King Aethelred's name and an English mint signature. Others bore the name of Sihtric III, King of Dublin. Coins of a standard size and weight offered a convenient means of exchange.

The Norse kings of Dublin for a while seem to have extended their control over the Isle of Man bringing greater prosperity to the island at the end of the tenth century. Soon afterwards, it has been suggested, a short-lived coinage based upon that of Dublin was introduced, reflecting close political contact between the two areas.

Hoards from Scotland contain a distinctive form of ring, introduced in the tenth century, which was used in the Earldom of Orkney as a form of currency at the same time as coins were being issued in Ireland. They appear in hoards from the Isle of Man dating to the eleventh century showing continuing contact with Scandinavian Scotland.

Irish Sea Trade

As Viking merchants sailed around the Irish Sea buying and selling goods they naturally saw and discussed new ideas and fashions with fellow travellers and tradesmen.

The fashion for wearing ringed pins to fasten heavy woollen or sheepskin cloaks was adopted by Norsemen from curren

Irish dress ornaments. A whole range of types developed with different designs. The plain-ringed polyhedral-headed variety, so called because of its many-sided pin-head, was first adopted by Norsemen in Ireland and from there the fashion spread to the Isle of Man, northern England and western Scotland, the Faroes and Iceland. An example has even been found in Newfoundland. By plotting the distribution of this form of dress fastener we can follow the northern and western sea routes travelled by Viking merchants during the tenth and eleventh centuries.

Ringed pins have been found in graves in Norway, Denmark and Sweden and, although some may represent loot from the Irish Sea region, others likewise were made in Scandinavia, where the fashion was copied.

A New Discovery

Thousands of warships and cargo vessels must have sailed through the Irish Sea during the Viking Age.

Only last year an exciting new discovery was made about a Viking warship, known as Skuldelev 2. It was one of five found twenty-five years ago forming a sunken blockade in Roskilde fjord, west of Copenhagen. Tests analysing the tree rings of the ship's oak keel have revealed fascinating results. The pattern of rings was most closely matched in Ireland, and Dublin in particular, where fragments of ships were uncovered during excavations and where it may well have been made c. AD 1060. This warship would have carried a crew of sixty warriors.

As research continues so our knowledge and understanding of the Viking Age increases.

Ringed pin from Chester.

Wooden plank bearing ship graffito found during excavations in Winetavern Street, Dublin.

VIKING-AGE SCULPTURE

The Gosforth cross is the largest surviving piece of sculpture from England from before the Norman Conquest. It is decorated with scenes from the Christian religion and Norse mythology.

Viking-Age Sculpture in the North West

Viking-age sculpture in the North West is a unique blend of Scandinavian, Anglian and Celtic traditions. The Vikings were converted to Christianity during the tenth and eleventh centuries and adopted the monastic tradition of setting up stone monuments to the memory of the dead.

Fragment of a cross from the church of St. Mary and St. Helen, Neston.

Prosperous merchants, tradesmen and wealthy farmers provided a ready market for craftsmen in stone. Workshops were established in towns such as York and Chester, but also in the countryside. Gosfort in Cumbria was one of the most important rural centres, still displaing work of the highest quality.

There were innovations in form and style and large numbers of monuments were carved. A new type of grave-cover, in the shape of contemporary Viking house with a shingle roof, was created in northern England, inspired by the stone shrines of the Anglo-Saxons.

Christian, pagan and secular subjects were depicted. Dramatic swirling beasts and gods, heroes and warriors provide a strong contrast with images of Christ or representations of the deceased.

Stone crosses and monuments identify areas of Viking settlement and influence, illustrating the close links which existed between the communities of the Irish Sea. A large number of particularly fine crosses survive in the Isle of Man, some bearing very complex and intricate designs.

Above all sculpture provides a lasting testimony to the presence of the Vikings on our shores.

Sculptors

The Vikings used bright colours to bring life and vitality to their stone monuments. Black, blue, red, brown, orange, yellow and white paints made it easier to appreciate detailed designs. Gesso, a form of plaster, was sometimes used as a base.

Crosses and grave-slabs were generally made from a single piece of local stone. Slate used by craftsmen in the Isle of Man seems to have been particularly suitable for creating very intricate patterns. It also proved ideal for carving runes.

Different workshops produced monuments with distinctive styles and designs. In the Isle of Man several of the crosses are associated with the work of one man, Gaut, who inscribed one of his stones as follows:

> 'This cross was erected by Melbrigdi, son of Adakan the Smith for his soul. Gaut made this and all in Man .'

In northern England it is clear that some craftsmen were using templates to create standard designs whereas other crosses are almost certainly individual to the people who commissioned them.

Artists took their inspiration from a variety of sources. Woodcarvings, designs on metalwork and illustrations in manuscripts could be copied and adapted.

Scandinavian Motifs and Mythology

Scandinavian art-styles and motifs were used to decorate stone crosses, though sometimes in a debased form. Some designs, such as the Borre style ring-chain, are common to both northern England and the Isle of Man suggesting a close cultural link between the two areas. There is a possibility that Gaut, the famous sculptor from the Isle of Man, spent his apprenticeship with master craftsmen in Cumbria.

Jellinge and Mammen art-styles are well represented on the Manx crosses. Interlaced beasts are found alongside episodes from Norse mythology. The Sigurd legend seems to have been a favourite of the

Gaut's cross with its distinctive ring chain pattern.

Sigurd roasts the dragon's
heart over the flames and
licks his burnt thumb.

settlers from Man. Sigurd was given the task of killing the dragon Fafnir because he had stolen a hoard of gold. Odin advised Sigurd to hide in a pit so that he could slay the dragon with his sword as it passed overhead. Having achieved his mission Sigurd roasted the dragon's heart.

Ragnarok, the tale of the overthrow and destruction of the gods is graphically illustrated on the Gosforth cross in Cumbria. In other regions images of Thor and Odin provide a link with the pagan past. Sometimes Christian and pagan scenes are combined, possibly to draw out the parallels which existed between the two religions, such as the struggle between good and evil.

Conversion to Christianity

When the Vikings arrived in the Irish Sea they found a region which had long since been converted to Christianity. Monasteries were the focus of the Christian religion, accumulating great wealth and attracting highly skilled craftsmen amongst whom were sculptors who carved monuments in stone. To the pagan Vikings these holy places were little more than unprotected storehouses of treasure.

But as the Vikings began to settle amongst these communities they too became converted to Christianity. Scandinavian kings were baptised, probably to gain favour with native populations with whom their followers intermarried and soon in both towns and villages new converts began setting up stone monuments in memory of the dead. Runic inscriptions on crosses in the Isle of Man bear both Celtic and Norse names showing how Norse farmers and warriors married native women.

Christian scenes on crosses depict the crucifixion and images of Christ in Majesty, as well as episodes from the Old Testament.

Many craftsmen were inspired by designs on Irish metalwork. This crucifixion plaque from Clonmacnoise, Ireland bears strong similarities to the design on the stone plaque from Penrith.

Stone plaque from Penrith, Cumbria showing the crucifixion of Christ.

THE END OF THE VIKING AGE

The Viking Age had come to an end by 1100 by which time Viking settlers and merchants in many areas had become absorbed into local populations. The Danes made one final attempt to gain control of England in AD 1085, but the planned invasion never took place. In Ireland Norse culture continued to flourish in coastal communities well into the twelfth century and Dublin was still Norse-speaking when it was invaded by the Anglo-Normans in AD 1170. It was only the Isle of Man and the Western Isles which remained under Norse control until the thirteenth century when the islands were finally handed over to the King of Scotland.

But our Viking heritage lives on in our language, in literature, in the sites and monuments which still surround the Irish Sea and in the artefacts which continue to be found. Only last year a hoard of five Irish and Viking silver brooches was discovered near Carlisle in Cumbria.

The Halton Moor hoard with its imported silver-gilt cup and spectacular neck-ring provides one final reminder of the wealth and of the craftsmanship of our Norse ancestors. An inspiration to us all!

The Halton Moor hoard was discovered in Lancashire in 1815. The magnificent silver-gilt cup is Carolingian in origin. It was found together with about 860 silver coins, a silver neck-ring and six gold foils.

LIST
OF
EXHIBITS

EXHIBITS

ENGLAND

CHESHIRE

Grosvenor Museum, Chester, Cheshire
Copper-alloy polyhedral-headed pins
166.S.1976; 168.S.1976
Copper-alloy ringed pin 171.S.1976

St. John's Church, Chester, Cheshire
Fragment of red sandstone circle-headed
cross (Tenth century)

St. Oswald's Church, Winwick, Cheshire
Millstone grit cross-arm of ring-headed
cross (Tenth century)

CUMBRIA

Bryant's Gill, Kentmere, Cumbria
SEARCH Archaeology Group, Cumbria
Gritstone whetstone in two pieces A 106;
A 174
Gritstone whetstone A 92
Iron auger A 169
Iron horseshoe A 8
Shale spindle whorl A 3
Shale spindle whorl A 46

St. James's Church, Burton-in-Kendal, Cumbria
Fragment of yellow sandstone cross-shaft
(Tenth-eleventh century)

St. Luke's Church, Clifton, Cumbria
Part of grey sandstone cross-shaft (Tenth
century)

St. John's Church, Cross Canonby, Cumbria
Fragment of red sandstone cross-shaft
(Tenth century)

St. Andrew's Church, Dacre, Cumbria
Complete yellow sandstone cross-shaft
(Tenth-eleventh century)

St. Mary's Churchyard, Gosforth, Cumbria (original)
Yorkshire Museum (cast)
Red sandstone ring-headed cross-shaft
(Tenth century)

Kirkoswald, Cumbria
British Museum
The Kirkoswald hoard, c.858-62
Anglo-Saxon silver trefoil ornament inlaid
with garnet OA.21

St. Michael's Church, Lowther, Cumbria
Fragments of red sandstone grave-cover
(Tenth century)

Nan Bield Pass, Cumbria
Carlisle Museums and Art Gallery
Iron spearhead 92-1971

Newbiggin Moor, Penrith, Cumbria
British Museum
Silver 'thistle' brooch 1909,6-24,2

Orton Scarr, Cumbria
The Orton Scarr hoard,
Society of Antiquaries of London
Silver bossed penannular brooch and
twisted neck-ring 366

Penrith, Cumbria
Abbot Hall Art Gallery, Kendal
Limestone plaque with an image of the
crucifixion (Tenth century) AH 2347/81

Scotby, near Carlisle, Cumbria
The Scotby hoard, c.935
Carlisle Museums and Art Gallery
Silver ingots and hacksilver 78-1935-32

GREATER MANCHESTER

Castlefield, Manchester, Greater Manchester
Manchester City Art Galleries
Silver-alloy disc with Anglo-Scandinavian
ornament 1909.408

KENT

Canterbury, Kent
Ashmolean Museum, Oxford
Anglo-Saxon silver nummular disc brooch
1951.131

LANCASHIRE

Cuerdale, Lancashire
The Cuerdale hoard, c.905
Ingots, ornaments and hacksilver

*Evans Collection, Ashmolean Museum,
Oxford 1909.519-551g
Assheton Collection, British Museum
1-163
British Museum 1841,7-11,1-741 & 1873,
Nelson Collection, Liverpool Museum
1953.114.24; 27-9; 32-42; 44-6; 48-63;
66
Society of Antiquaries, London 885
National Museums of Scotland, IM 24-26
Fitzwilliam Museum, Cambridge 708:1-10
University Museum of Archaeology and
Anthropology, Cambridge 1939.43*

Cuerdale, Lancashire
The Cuerdale hoard, c.905
Mr Swarbrick
Bone pins

Cuerdale, Lancashire
The Cuerdale hoard, c.905
*Related watercolours, manuscripts and
memorabilia*

Assheton Collection, British Museum
Rosewood cabinet presented to William
Assheton by the Duchy of Lancaster

Harris Museum and Art Gallery, Preston
Watercolour of the Bull Inn, Preston by J.
Ferguson 1853

Private Lender
Drawing of Cuerdale by William
Assheton c.1790

Private Lender
Necklace of silver pennies from the hoard
presented to Mr Teesdale

*HM the Queen in right of Her Duchy of
Lancaster*
Coloured survey of the River Ribble, by
William Millar of Preston 1840 (B3)
Treasure trove declaration (B3)
The Brief prepared by Mr Teesdale,
Duchy solicitor (B8)
Letter bearing the Duchy of Lancaster's
seal (B8)
Short report on the contents and value of
the hoard prepared for Queen Victoria
(B3)
Report on the contents of the Cuerdale
hoard (B7)
Duchy of Lancaster distribution lists of
Anglo-Saxon and Continental coins (B8)
Letter from William Assheton to the
Duchy of Lancaster, 19th August 1840 (B1)
Letter from Edward Hawkins to the Duchy
of Lancaster, 2nd September 1840 (B1)
Letter from Jonathan Richardson to the
Duchy of Lancaster, October 1840 (B1)
Letter from the Royal Institution,
Liverpool, 11th November 1841 (B5)
Receipt for coins from the Royal
Institution, Liverpool, 24th November
1841 (B5)
Letter accompanying the presentation of
coins and ingots to the Cambridge
Antiquarian Society, 29th June 1844 (B3)
Receipt from the Cambridge Antiquarian
Society for twenty coins and twelve
ingots, 4th July 1844 (B3)
Letter from Mr Akerman of the
Numismatic Society of London (B2)
Formal receipt for coins from the
Numismatic Society of London (B4)

Claughton Hall, Garstang, Lancashire
*Harris Museum and Art Gallery, Preston
(Mr Fitzherbert-Brockholes)*
Female grave group
Pair of gilt copper-alloy oval brooches
Silver gilt mount
Glass beads

Claughton Hall, Garstang, Lancashire
Harris Museum and Art Gallery, Preston
Bound watercolours of gravegoods found at Claughton Hall, Lancashire, by John Weld 1834

Society of Antiquaries, London
Watercolour of gravegoods found at Claughton Hall, Lancashire by Edward Jones 1846, Brown portfolio 8.30

Halton Moor, Lancashire
The Halton Moor hoard, c.1025
British Museum
Carolingian silver-gilt cup
Plaited silver neck-ring
Gold foils
AF.541-2; OA.3393

St. Patrick's Chapel, Heysham, Lancashire
Lancaster City Museums
Grave find
Bone comb 87.52

Saddleworth, Lancashire
British Museum
Gold finger-ring 1915,12-6,1

MERSEYSIDE

Harkirk, Little Crosby, Merseyside
Mrs Whitlock Blundell, Lancashire Record Office
Notebook in which William Blundell recorded finds from the Harkirk hoard DDBL 6121

St.Mary and St. Helen's Church, Neston, Wirral
Fragments of red sandstone shaft of circle-headed cross (Tenth century)

Meols, Wirral, Merseyside
Grosvenor Museum, Chester
Copper-alloy ringed pin 169.S.1976
Copper-alloy ringed pin 174.S.1976

Meols, Wirral, Merseyside
Liverpool Museum
Copper-alloy buckle with Ringerike-style bird-head decoration M5689

St. Bridget's Church, West Kirby, Wirral, Merseyside
Complete white sandstone hogback with wheel and bar ornament (Tenth century)

NORTH YORKSHIRE

Bolton Percy, North Yorkshire
The Bolton Percy hoard, pre-867
Yorkshire Museum
Northumbrian copper stycas 1967.6
Pot containing hoard 1967.6

Bossall Flaxton, North Yorkshire
The Bossall/Flaxton hoard, c.927
Yorkshire Museum
Silver arm-ring 700.48

Goldsborough, North Yorkshire
The Goldsborough hoard, c.920
British Museum
Silver brooches and hacksilver 1859, 5-11,1-11

Goldsborough, North Yorkshire
The Goldsborough hoard,c.920
The Churchwardens, St Mary's Church, Goldsborough
Silver pendant cross

Goldsborough, North Yorkshire
The Goldsborough hoard, c.920
Society of Antiquaries of London
Pencil drawing of lost ingots from the hoard MS 700/6

Ribblehead, North Yorkshire
Yorkshire Museum
Iron bell 1985.29
Iron knife blades 1985.29
Stone quern 1985.29
Stone spindle whorl 1985.29

Sawdon, North Yorkshire
Yorkshire Museum
Bone sleeve with Mammen decoration 632.48

Whitby Abbey, North Yorkshire,
(raided by the Vikings in AD 867)
British Museum
Anglo-Saxon Trewhiddle-style silver roundel and strap-end 10/W.32; W.52

York, North Yorkshire
Yorkshire Museum
Borre-style lead die for pendant 702.4.48
Coin die for St Peter's penny (replica) 1980.7.125630
Copper-alloy pin with flat head H2000
Copper-alloy ringed pin 622.48
Cresset stone lamp 22
Iron axe 551.48.48
Lead strip with coin impression (replica) 1979.7.17692

Lead strip with coin impression (replica) 1980.7.125350
Pair of bone skates 1971.321
Pewter disc brooch with animal design 652.48
Silver disc brooch with an image of Emperor Valentinian 701.48

No. 5 Coppergate, York
Yorkshire Museum
Leather shoe 1974.8.11

Coppergate, York
Yorkshire Museum
Iron flesh fork 551.50.48
Iron axe 643.48.48

Blake Street, York
Yorkshire Museum
Copper-alloy balance 1975.6.82

Clifford Street, York
Yorkshire Museum
Antler tines C603-4; C587/3
Bone buckles C617.48; C618,48
Bone comb plate C650.3
Bone face C626.48
Bone pin with flat head C533
Bone pipe C663
Clay lamp C672.48
Glass linen smoother 1948.6.4
Iron fish hook 1974.21.5409
Iron knives with bone handles C620.48; C662
Stone net weight sinker C658
Unfinished amber C618a; C621e; C621g
Unworked amber C598b, C599a, b, d
Wooden spoons C628-9

Coppergate, York
York City Council, Yorkshire Museum
Amber beads 1976.7.302; 606; 1979.7.893; 1697; 2116; 2160; 4201; 1980.7.8564
Antler comb 1980.7.8481
Antler comb case 1979.7.7284
Antler plates for combs 1979.7.6857; 1980.7.8595
Antler weaving tablet 1980.7.8476
Bone comb 1979.7.5704
Bone crutch-headed pin 1977.7.1763
Bone strap-end 1979.7. 6833
Bone, antler and chalk gaming pieces 1979.9.8169; 1979.7.4949; 6739; 1980.7.8234
Bone, stone and antler spindle whorls 1978.7.2903; 2534; 1980.7.11321; 1986.7.9514; 1977.7.1554
Child's leather ankle boot 1977.7.4422
Clay loom weights 1979.7.7003; 1981.7.12676; 12781
Copper-alloy balance 1980.7.7576

Copper-alloy ringed pin 1977.7.774
Copper-alloy strap-end with openwork decoration 1980.7.7501
Copper-alloy ring 1980.7.7806
Copper-alloy coated iron weights 1981.7.15880; 15879
Fragment of Badorf ware from the Rhineland 1979.7.14626
Fragment of Pingsdorf ware from the Rhineland 1980.7.18814
Fragment of Stamford ware from Lincolnshire 1980.7.18815
Glass beads 1976.7.308; 393; 426; 1977.7.1734; 2215; 1979.7.5013; 5085; 5354; 6584; 6637; 6916
Gold ear-ring 1979.7.4103
Iron chisel 1980.7.10108
Iron fish hook 1978.7.3347
Iron keys 1978.7.3265; 1978.7.9336
Iron needles 1980.7.11454; 8004
Iron shears 1980.7.9876
Iron spoon-bit 1980.7.9071
Jet finger-rings 1979.7.5381; 7080
Jet roughout 1980.7.9181
Lava quern 1979.7.4706
Lead strap-end 1979.7.7306
Lead-alloy arm-ring 1980.7.8502
Lead-alloy disc brooch 1980.7.7548
Lead-alloy 'ship' pendant 1980.7.7606
Leather offcut with Jellinge decoration 1981.7.16278
Leather shoe 1980.7.7663
Leather shoe 1980.7.9804
Leather offcuts 1977.7.850
Slate whetstone 1980.7.8946
Small wooden dish 1977.7.859
Soapstone bowl fragment 1980.7.7565
Torksey ware spouted pitcher from Lincolnshire 1979.7
Unfinished wooden bowl 1977.8.980
Unworked jet 1978.7.4285; 1980.7.7907; 1980.7.9181
Whetstone 1980.7.140
Wooden barrel lid 1980.7.14527
Wooden beaker 1977.7.1384
Wooden bowl 1979.7.4085
Wooden cores 1979.7.4689; 5281; 4837
Wooden pan pipes 1979.7.5083
Wooden saddle bow 1977.7.1745
Y-shaped antler tine 1980.7.9931
York ware cooking pot 1980.7.26721

Coppergate, York
Yorkshire Museum
Unfinished limestone slab carved in Jellinge style (Early-mid tenth century) 1977.7.2115

Goodramgate, York
Yorkshire Museum

Wooden spindle 555.8.48
Hungate, York
Yorkshire Museum
Gold finger-ring 726.48
Iron padlock 1971.321

Market Street and Bedern, York
Yorkshire Museum
Bone pins 1955.10.6; 1951.21

Nunnery Lane, York
Yorkshire Museum
Bone part of ship's rigging 574.48

Parliament Street, York
Yorkshire Museum
Leather scabbards 1976.11.47; 73

6-8 Pavement, York
Yorkshire Museum
Cloth fragment 1972.21.5265
Iron awl 1974.21.5403
Wooden shoe last 1972.21

Pavement, York
Yorkshire Museum
Bundle of yarn 1974.21.5331
Copper-alloy disc brooch 1951.52.3
Silk fragment 1972.21
Wooden knife handle decorated with Ringerike design 1987.21

Railway Station, York
Yorkshire Museum
Jet snake pendant H110

St. Mary Bishophill Senior, York
Yorkshire Museum
Borre-style strap-end 1973.24

St. Denys's Churchyard, York
Yorkshire Museum
Fragment of freestone grave-slab (Tenth century) 1985.28

Near Malton, North Yorkshire
Iron spearhead 1986.27

Weston Church, North Yorkshire
Yorkshire Museum
(Lt.Col.H.V.Dawson)
Gritstone slab (Tenth century)

OXFORDSHIRE

Near Oxford, Oxfordshire
Liverpool Museum
Silver 'Hiberno-Viking' arm-ring, incorrectly provenanced to the Cuerdale hoard 1953.114.23

STAFFORDSHIRE

Beeston Tor Cave, Staffordshire
The Beeston Tor hoard c.875
British Museum

Anglo-Saxon silver disc brooches and rings 1925,1-14,1-2; 1925,2-17,1-3
Copper-alloy strip of metal sheet 1925,1-14,3

SURREY

Croydon (Whitehorse), Surrey
The Croydon hoard, c.872
Ashmolean Museum, Oxford
Silver 'Hiberno-Viking' style arm-ring, spiral ring fragments and ingots 1909.556-61

ISLE OF MAN

Isle of Man
The Manx Museum and National Trust
Watercolour of the Promulgation of Laws on Tynwald Hill attributed to John 'Warwick' Smith, 1749-1831 7219

Knock-y-Doonee, Andreas, Isle of Man
The Manx Museum and National Trust
Male grave find (boat burial)
Lead fishing weight 2774/26

Chapel Hill, Balladoole, Arbory, Isle of Man
The Manx Museum and National Trust
Male grave find (boat burial)
Carolingian copper-alloy spur mounts and strap-ends 66-372-19; 20; 21; 22
Carolingian silver-gilt buckle and strap-end 66-372-23; 24
Copper-alloy harness-mounts 66-372-5D-G; J-M; P-Q
Copper-alloy mounts with enamelling 66-372-7
Copper-alloy ringed pin 66-372-32
Flint strike-a-light 66-372-31
Stone hone 66-372-30

Ballaquayle, Douglas, Isle of Man
The Douglas hoard, c.970
The Manx Museum and National Trust and British Museum
Gold and silver rings, ring-money and hacksilver 4408-19; 4421 & 1895,8-9,1-8

Near Greeba, German, Isle of Man
The Manx Museum and National Trust
Plaited gold finger-ring 83-12

Ballateare, Jurby, Isle of Man
The Manx Museum and National Trust
Male grave find
Iron shield boss 66-373-8A

Cronk Mooar, Jurby, Isle of Man
The Manx Museum and National Trust
Male grave group
Copper-alloy ringed pin 66-374-10
Fragment of cloth 66-374-11
Reconstruction of Cronk Mooar cloak
fragment 66-374-11b

Larivane, Kirk Andreas, Isle of Man
The Manx Museum and National Trust
Fragment of slate cross-slab (Tenth
century) 193

Kirk Andreas, Isle of Man
The Manx Museum and National Trust
Slate cross-slab fragment (cast) (Tenth
century) 121

Kirk Andreas, Isle of Man
The Manx Museum and National Trust
Slate cross-slab fragment (cast) 128

Kirk Braddan, Isle of Man
The Manx Museum and National Trust
Slate circle-headed cross with insular
Jellinge/Mammen ornament (cast) (Late
tenth-early eleventh century) 135

Kirk Michael, Isle of Man
The Kirk Michael hoard, c.1065
The Manx Museum and National Trust
Silver ring-money and coins 76-85;
76-86; 76-87
Fragment of cloth (hoard container)
76-90

Kirk Michael, Isle of Man
The Manx Museum and National Trust
Slate cross-slab with Borre-style ornament
(cast) (Tenth century) 101

Kirk Michael, Isle of Man
The Manx Museum and National Trust
Circle-headed cross-slab with insular
Mammen/Ringerike ornament (cast)
(Early eleventh century)

Ronaldsway, Malen, Isle of Man
The Manx Museum and National Trust
Copper-alloy beam balance with lead
weight 64-144/224

**Peel Castle, St. Patrick's Isle, Isle
of Man**
The Manx Museum and National Trust
Grave group
Copper-alloy buckle 84.16.420 MW
Copper-alloy ringed pin 84.16.420 LQ
Silver wire balls from cloak 84.16.420
MVa-d
Silver penny of Eadmund, 939-46
84.16L.420
Pagan lady's' grave
Ammonite fossil 84.16L.483 G

Bone comb 84.16L.483 JL
Copper-alloy needles 84.16L 483 OA-B
Iron knife 84.16L 483 JM
Iron shears 84.16L 483 JK
Miniature stone pestle and mortar 84.16L
483 IT

Grave group
Copper-alloy ringed pin 85.60L 1198 OR
Copper-alloy buckle/strap-end set 85.60L
1198 OP/OL

Child's grave
Copper-alloy bell with iron clapper
84.16L 758

Grave find
Copper-alloy tweezers 86.53H 542 IL
Copper-alloy stick-pin 86.53H 542 IS

Grave find
Copper-alloy key 84.16B 303 HP
Silver 'ring-money' fragment 55.334

SCOTLAND

Scotland
British Museum
Silver 'Hiberno-Viking' arm-rings
1851,7-15,8-9

Scotland
*National Museums of Scotland,
Edinburgh*
Copper-alloy ringed pins GT 971; GT 973

**Glenn Fruinn, Near Loch
Lomond, Central**
Watercolour of grave goods found near
Boiden, Lower Bridge, Glenn Fruinn, near
Loch Lomond, artist unknown c.1882 MS
498

**Tundergarth, Dumfries and
Galloway**
British Museum
Gold finger-ring AF.466

**Whithorn Priory, Wigtown,
Dumfries and Galloway**
The Whithorn Trust
Antler comb 86/702
Antler working debris 89/10991; 88/9300;
88/9267/1; 88/9033; 88/9109/1;
88/9144/4; 88/9377/2 88/9305/4;
88/9322/4; 88/9332/5; 88/9330/2;
88/9358/1; 87/4589; 87/4589/5
Clay crucible 86/1049/1
Copper-alloy ringed pin 87/3452
Copper-alloy stick-pins 86/508; 881; 715;
366; 36/1020/1; 87/2505; 3657; 3335;
3117
Glass tesserae 87/2347; 3211; 4343;
2582; 3551; 4635; 2930; 3860; 4136;
7149

Haematite ore 86/1579; 88/6962; 7106
Lead basin 86/648/1
Leadworking debris 86/933/3; 86/547/1;
87/3129
Leatherworking offcuts 87/4186
Rotary grindstone 87/4312
Skull of a cat 87/3116
Sole of a leather shoe 86/846/1
Stone grooved hone 85/715

Clatchard's Craig, Fife
National Museums of Scotland
Pictish fort
Clay moulds for brooches HHC 58-9
Enamelled mount HHC 122
Silver ingot HHC 121

**Croy, near Inverness, Highlands
and Islands**
*National Museums of Scotland,
Edinburgh*
Pictish hoard, c.845
Copper-alloy beam balance FC 15

Talnotrie, Kirkcudbrightshire
The Talnotrie hoard, c.875
*National Museums of Scotland,
Edinburgh*
Anglo-Saxon silver ornaments and
miscellaneous objects FC 198-225

Dunadd, Argyll, Strathclyde
*National Museums of Scotland,
Edinburgh*
Scottish fort
Bone motif piece GP 195
Clay brooch mould GP 221
Clay crucibles GP 222; 224
Stone ingot mould GP 203

Port Glasgow, Strathclyde
The Port Glasgow hoard, c.970
*National Museums of Scotland,
Edinburgh*
Twisted and plain silver arm-rings IL
225-6

HEBRIDES

Hebrides
*National Museums of Scotland,
Edinburgh* Hoard, 10/11th cent.
Gold plaited rings and ingots FE 17-26

Inchkenneth, Argyll, Hebrides
The Inchkenneth hoard, c.1000
British Museum
Silver chain 1851,6-13,1

Iona, Argyll, Hebrides
The Iona hoard, c.986
*National Museums of Scotland,
Edinburgh*
Hacksilver IL 715-7

Ardvonrig, Barra, Hebrides
British Museum
Female grave find
Pair of copper-alloy oval brooches
1895,6-13,1-2

Kilbar, Barra, Hebrides
*National Museums of Scotland,
Edinburgh*
Cross-slab with runic inscription (Tenth
century) IB 102

Inchmarnoch, Bute, Hebrides
*National Museums of Scotland,
Edinburgh*
Slate cross-slab with runic inscription
(Tenth century) IB 193

Kiloran Bay, Colonsay, Hebrides
*National Museums of Scotland,
Edinburgh*
Male grave find (boat burial)
Copper-alloy beam balance and scale
pans IL 774/1 196; IL 775/1; IL 776
Lead weights IL 777-783
Copper-alloy buckle and mount IL 796
Copper-alloy mounts IL 785-9
Copper-alloy strap mounts IL 791-5
Copper-alloy ringed pin IL 784
Iron axehead IL 761/1
Iron boat rivets IL 773/1-10
Iron shield boss IL 762/1

*National Museums of Scotland,
Edinburgh*
Watercolour of Viking boat burial at
Kiloran Bay, Colonsay, by McNeil and
Galloway 1882-3 1882/3

Society of Antiquaries, London
Watercolour of Viking boat burial at
Kiloran Bay, Colonsay, by W. Galloway
1883 Brown portfolio L5.72
Watercolour of scales and weights found
at Kiloran Bay, Colonsay, by Rosa Wallis
c.1885 Brown portfolio 20.71
Watercolour of weapons found at Kiloran
Bay, Colonsay, by Rosa Wallis 1883
Brown portfolio 20.71
Watercolour of harness mounts found at
Kiloran Bay, Colonsay, by Rosa Wallis
1883 Brown portfolio 20.71

Eigg, Hebrides
*National Museums of Scotland,
Edinburgh*
Male grave find
Copper-alloy sword hilt with silver and
niello decoration IL 157
Bog-find
Wooden stempost from a ship (replica)
IN 4

Kildonan, Eigg, Hebrides
*National Museums of Scotland,
Edinburgh*
Grave find
Cloth fragments IL 164a-d

Fladda Chuin, Hebrides
*National Museums of Scotland,
Edinburgh*
Gold plaited finger-ring FE 31

Boreray, Harris, Hebrides
*National Museums of Scotland,
Edinburgh*
Copper-alloy ringed pin GT 238

Islay, Hebrides
*National Museums of Scotland,
Edinburgh*
Female grave find
Pair of copper-alloy oval brooches IL
215-6

Ballinaby, Islay, Hebrides
*National Museums of Scotland,
Edinburgh*
Copper-alloy ringed pin IL 384

Ballinaby I, Islay, Hebrides
*National Museums of Scotland,
Edinburgh*
Male grave find
Iron adze IL 134
Iron axehead IL 131
Iron hammerhead IL 133
Iron shield boss IL 126

Ballinaby II, Islay, Hebrides
*National Museums of Scotland,
Edinburgh*
Female grave find
Copper-alloy ladle IL 147
Glass beads IL 149; 150; 152; 153/1-4;
154/1-6
Glass linen smoother IL 148
Pair of copper-alloy oval brooches IL
138-9
Silver chain IL 146a,b,c
Silver pin IL 145

**Doid Mhairi, Port Ellen, Islay,
Hebrides**
*National Museums of Scotland,
Edinburgh*
Sandstone cross-slab with Ringerike
ornament (Late tenth-early eleventh
century) IB 193

Kneep, Uig, Lewis, Hebrides
*National Museums of Scotland,
Edinburgh*
Female grave find
Pair of oval copper-alloy brooches IL

799-800
Bone comb IL 845
Bone needle case IL 848
Copper-alloy ringed pin IL 852
Copper-alloy belt buckle IL 853
Copper-alloy strap-end IL 854
Glass beads IL 801-44
Whetstone IL 847

The Udal, North Uist, Hebrides
The Udal Research Programme
Bone combs 8033; 10220; 5067; 8179;
12576; 12837
Bone comb case 6750
Bone pins 10434; 11384; 9395; 9960;
10500; 9107; 10378; 9052
Clay crucibles 10112; 13704
Copper-alloy harness stud with leather
strap 5036
Copper-alloy pin 18629
Copper-alloy stick-pins 18170; 8818;
8321; 4989; 4967;
Copper-alloy strap-end with Borre
decoration 10746
Fragments of clay moulds 13705; 16275
Fragments of pottery platter with seed
and textile impressions 7743
Iron casket mount with silver inlay 9342
Silver penny of Harald Hardrada, King of
Norway, 1055-65 8004

**Carn a'Bharraich, Oronsay,
Hebrides**
*National Museums of Scotland,
Edinburgh*
Female grave find
Pair of copper-alloy oval brooches IL
329-30
Bone needle case IL 332
Copper-alloy knob-ringed pin IL 331

**Storr Rock, Trotternish, Isle of
Skye, Hebrides**
The Storr Rock hoard, c.935
*National Museums of Scotland,
Edinburgh*
Silver ingots and hacksilver IL 282-304

ORKNEY

Skaill, Sandwick, Orkney
The Skaill hoard, c.950
*National Museums of Scotland,
Edinburgh*
Selection of silver ring-money IL 26; 28;
41; 42a

Burray, Orkney
The Burray hoard, c.1000
*National Museums of Scotland,
Edinburgh*
Selection of silver ring-money IL 238-9;
245; 254; 256; 260

SHETLAND

St. Ninian's Isle, Shetland
National Museums of Scotland,
Edinburgh
Pictish hoard
Pictish silver bowl with interlace ornament
FC 274
Pictish silver penannular brooches FC
292; FC 294

IRELAND

Ireland
National Museum of Ireland, Dublin
Silver 'Hiberno-Viking' arm-rings W.63;
W.77; W.92; W.98
Silver Baltic silver penannular brooch
fragment W.60
Silver 'Permian' spiral ring terminal
fragment W.59
Silver 'thistle' brooch W.38
Silver Irish bossed penannular brooch
P.742
Silver Irish bossed penannular brooch
W.35
Silver Irish pseudo-penannular brooch
with disc terminals W.29; 30
Silver ribbon bracelet W.76

Ireland
National Museums of Scotland,
Edinburgh
Silver Irish bossed penannular brooch
FD 1

Ireland
British Museum
Silver 'Hiberno-Viking' arm-ring
1871,4-1,16

Forkhill, Co. Armagh
Liverpool Museum
Silver finger-ring 1953.114.43

Virginia, Co. Cavan
British Museum
Plaited gold arm-ring 1849,3-1,2

Roosky, Co. Donegal
The Roosky hoard, c.9/10th. cent.
National Museum of Ireland, Dublin
Silver 'Hiberno-Viking' arm-rings, plain
and twisted silver rings 1966.21-4

Newry, Co. Down
National Museum of Ireland, Dublin
Silver ingots W.3; W.4

Near Galway, Co. Galway
National Museum of Ireland, Dublin
Silver double arm-ring W.72

Ballyadams, Co. Laois
National Museum of Ireland, Dublin
Silver bullion ring and ingot W.7; W.32

Richardstown, Co. Louth
National Museum of Ireland, Dublin
Silver 'thistle' brooch 1964.239

Lagore, Co. Meath
National Museum of Ireland, Dublin
Clay crucibles E1.402; E1.431

Moynagh, Co. Meath
National Museum of Ireland, Dublin
Stone ingot mould 1887.45

Clonmacnoise, Co. Offaly
National Museum of Ireland, Dublin
Irish copper-alloy crucifixion plaque
R.2917

Carrick, Co. Westmeath
The Carrick hoard, c.9/10th. cent.
National Museum of Ireland, Dublin
Selection of native Irish silver ingots
1981:1-6

Creaghduff, Co. Westmeath
The Creaghduff hoard, c.9/10th cent.
National Museum of Ireland, Dublin
Silver 'Hiberno-Viking' arm-ring and
ingot fragments 1988.223a-j

Dysart Island, Lough Ennell, Co. Westmeath
The Dysart Island no. 4 hoard, c.905/10
National Museum of Ireland, Dublin
Silver ingots and hacksilver 1981.297

Waterford, Co. Waterford
British Museum
Gold finger-ring 1849,3-1,20

DUBLIN
National Museum of Ireland, Dublin
Decorated wooden finial 1887.144

Christchurch Place, Dublin
National Museum of Ireland, Dublin
Copper-alloy Borre-style belt-end
E122.17157
Iron sickle with wooden handle
E122.6558
Thor's hammer, crucifix and ingot mould
E122.14318
Wooden plane with animal head and
runic inscription E122.13655

Fishamble Street and High Street, Dublin
National Museum of Ireland, Dublin
Amber illustrating the manufacturing
process E172.15109; 10220; 10728;
8078; E141.5062; E71.16769
Wood, clay and bone gaming pieces

E148.819; E172.830; E190.3360;
E190.3837; E71.5107

Fishamble Street and John's Lane, Dublin
National Museum of Ireland, Dublin
Copper-alloy and iron needles
E190.2504; E173.3793

Fishamble Street and Winetavern Street, Dublin
National Museum of Ireland, Dublin
Bone motif pieces E148.1127; E190.148;
E81.1734
Copper-alloy strap-ends E190.7045;
E81.581

Fishamble Street, Dublin
National Museum of Ireland,
Bone weaving tablets E190.7234;
E190.2104
Copper-alloy needle E190.2504
Copper-alloy ringed pins E141.3666;
E172.14237
Copper-alloy stick-pin E190.6232;
E172.10020
Glass beads E172.14003; E190.7254;
E190.7648; E190.800. E190.6369
Bone and stone spindle whorls
E190.4534; E172.11146; E190.4609
Bone belt-end E172.11275
Bone buzzdiscs E172.6641
Bone comb E172.12616
Bone comb case E172.16135
Bone pin E190.1884
Copper-alloy Borre-style strap-end
E190.5327
Copper-alloy ball of interwoven wire
E172.11170
Copper-alloy kite-shaped brooch
E172.5791
Copper-alloy, jet and amber finger-rings
E190.2871; E172.10803; E141.4623
Crowland-type pottery sherd E190.2521
Fragment of Chester ware E172.14279
Fragment of cloth E190.4563
Fragment of porphyry marble E172.2927
Fragment of tablet-woven braid
E172.12347
Fragments of jet bracelet E172.13939
Iron knives E172.11599; E141.1300
Iron needle E173.3793
Iron padlock E172.14662
Lead and pewter Winchester-style mount
E190.740
Leather knife scabbard E141.1317
Rotary sharpening stone E190.27
Jet illustrating the manufacturing process
E172.10554; 7730; 10219; E190.6401;
E71.9981
Silk bonnet E172.10540

Silk ribbon E172.9951
Unfinished bone gaming pieces
E190.3967; E172.14355
Walrus ivory E172.4311
Wooden bucket stave with iron handle
E172.13095
Wooden card and thread E141.3332
Wooden net float E172.5792
Wooden platter E172.6656
Wooden spoons E172.1342; E172.1547
Wooden stave with animal head
E141.5106
Wooden stool E172.11974

High Street and Fishamble Street, Dublin
National Museum of Ireland, Dublin
Copper-alloy toilet set E43.1922;
E190.5326

High Street, Dublin
National Museum of Ireland, Dublin
Child's leather boot E71.2093
Iron fork E43.665
Iron key E71.3657
Lead boat-shaped weight E71.13116
Leather shoe with lace E71.16870
Iron shears E71.3750
Pewter disc brooch E71.19552
Wooden bowl E71.12006
Wooden fragment decorated in the
Urnes style E71.6180
Wooden spade E71.16348

John's Lane, Dublin
National Museum of Ireland, Dublin
Copper-alloy bracelet E173.3370
Leather knife scabbard E173.3602
Wooden weaving batten E173.4388

Kilmainham-Islandbridge, Dublin
Viking cemetery, 9th cent.
National Museum of Ireland, Dublin
Copper-alloy balance scales R.420
Copper-alloy belt buckle R.2378-9;
R.2407
Copper-alloy ring brooch-pin 1885.120
Glass and amber beads 1881.486-94
Glass linen smoother W.122
Iron sickle Wk.32
Iron sword inlaid with silver Wk.9
Iron sword with copper-alloy hilt inlaid
with silver and niello Wk.33
Iron shield bosses Wk.2; Wk.10
Iron tongs Wk.36
Pair of copper-alloy oval brooches
R.2420
Whalebone gaming pieces D.336-9
Whalebone plaque, probably used as an
ironing board W.70-72

Male grave group
Casket handles 1933.11
Iron axehead 1933.9
Iron fire steel 1933.10
Iron nails 1933.12-15
Iron spearhead 1933.8
Iron sword 1933.16

Watercolour of weapons and tools from
Kilmainham-Islandbridge cemetery by
James Plunkett, 1847

Winetavern Street, Dublin
National Museum of Ireland, Dublin
Copper-alloy buckle E81.5572
Decorated French pottery sherd
E81.4634
Iron awl with wooden handle E81.535
Wooden plank with ship graffito (replica)
E81.5327
Wooden toy boat E81.432

Wood Quay, Dublin
National Museum of Ireland, Dublin
Wooden box E132.18787
Wooden gaming board E132.55185

WALES

Dinorben Quarry, Anglesey
The Anglesey hoard, c.9th/10th cent.
National Museum of Wales, Cardiff
Silver 'Hiberno-Viking' arm-rings
28.215/1-5

Bangor, Gwynedd
The Bangor 'Midland Bank' hoard, c.925
Museum of Welsh Antiquities, Bangor
Silver coins and hacksilver 85.17H

EUROPE

BALTIC

Perm Area, East Baltic
British Museum
Silver neck-ring 1878,5-9,3

NORWAY

Historisk Museum, University of Bergen
Iron swords (replica)
Iron shield bosses (replica)
Iron spearheads (replica)
Iron arrowheads (replica)
Iron axe (replica)
Iron horsebit (replica)
Iron knife (replica)
Wooden spindle with steatite whorl
(replica)

HORDALAND, NORWAY

Leirvåg, Austrheim, Hordaland

Historisk Museum, University of Bergen
Soapstone saucepan B 6671

Dale, Fjaler, Hordaland
Historisk Museum, University of Bergen
Female grave find
Glass linen smoother B 5910s

Eidfjord, Hordaland
Historisk Museum, University of Bergen
Copper-alloy penannular brooch B 3872

Osnes, Etne, Hordaland
The Osnes hoard, 9th/10th cent.
Historisk Museum, University of Bergen
Silver 'Hiberno-Viking' style arm-ring
fragments and plain linked rings
B 2213-21

Hellevik, Holmedal, Fjaler, Hordaland
Historisk Museum, University of Bergen
Copper-alloy arm-ring B 3360

Kollsøyo, Fjellberg, Hordaland
Historisk Museum, University of Bergen
Soapstone bowl B 11495

Nes, Kvinnherad, Hordaland
Historisk Museum, University of Bergen
Male grave find
Heavy iron hammer B 4472

Netteland, Kvinnherad, Hordaland
Historisk Museum, University of Bergen
Iron gouge with modern handle B 5775

Keilegavlen, Lindås, Hordaland
Historisk Museum, University of Bergen
Steatite ingot mould B 7996

Seim, Odda, Hordaland
Historisk Museum, University of Bergen
Female grave find
Gilt-copper-alloy mount from a cross-arm
B 492

Hatteberg, Rosendal, Hordaland
The Hatteberg hoard, c.9th/10th cent.
Historisk Museum, University of Bergen
Silver 'Hiberno-Viking' style bossed
penannular brooch B 8377c
Plaited silver neck-ring B 8377b
Twisted gold arm-ring B 8377a

Lekve, Ulvik, Hordaland
Historisk Museum, University of Bergen
Grave find
Iron cauldron B 5400
Longhandled iron frying pan B 5490
Longhandled iron saucepan B 5490a

Bakketun, Voss, Hordaland
Historisk Museum, University of Bergen
Silver ingot B 738

Bryn, Voss, Hordaland
Historisk Museum, University of Bergen
Male grave find
Iron rasp B 3987

Fitje, Voss, Hordaland
Historisk Museum, University of Bergen
Grave find
Iron tongs B 4155

Vangen, Voss, Hordaland
Historisk Museum, University of Bergen
Male grave find
Light iron hammer
B 2758

VEST-AGDER

Vestre Rom, Lyngdal, Vest Agder
The Vestre Rom hoard, 9th/10th cent.
Historisk Museum, University of Bergen
Silver arm-rings B 5809

NORD-TRØNDELAG

Verdalen, Nord-Trøndelag
Historisk Museum, University of Bergen
Silver Thor's hammer pendant B 8602

NORDLAND

Nordland
Historisk Museum, University of Bergen
Silver ringed pin B 5886

Nes, Hamarøy, Nordland
Historisk Museum, University of Bergen
Grave find
Ivory dice and bone gaming pieces
(replica) Original B 5161

Meløy, Rødøy, Nordland
Historisk Museum, University of Bergen
Female grave find
Copper-alloy mount with amber and blue
glass inlay, re-used as a brooch B 5393

OPPLAND

Olberg, Slidre, Oppland
Historisk Museum, University of Bergen
Gilt copper-alloy hinge mount from a
shrine B 3421

ROGALAND

Re, Hå, Rogaland
Historisk Museum, University of Bergen
Grave find
Gold ingot B 2521

Rossebø, Haugesund, Rogaland
Historisk Museum, University of Bergen
Silver trefoil-headed pin B 4385

Hetland, Hetland, Rogaland

Historisk Museum, University of Bergen
Silver 'Hiberno-Viking' style arm-ring
B 483

Mosnaes, Hjelmeland, Rogaland
Historisk Museum, University of Bergen
Silver trefoil brooch B 4342

Hauge, Klepp, Rogaland
Historisk Museum, University of Bergen
Gold foil representing Frey and the
giantess Gerd B 5392

Orre, Klepp, Rogaland
Historisk Museum, University of Bergen
Glass, agate and clay beads B 2577

Orre, Klepp, Rogaland
Historisk Museum, University of Bergen
Female grave find Gilt copper-alloy
harness mount B 2561

Jåtten, Stavanger, Rogaland
Historisk Museum, University of Bergen
Tin-coated copper-alloy scales with lead
weights B 4772

Herbakken, Suldal, Rogaland
Historisk Museum, University of Bergen
Twisted silver arm-ring B 481

Horr, Varhaug, Rogaland
Historisk Museum, University of Bergen
Silver cross B 5307

MØRE OG ROMSDAL

**Ringstad, Stranda, Møre og
Romsdal**
Historisk Museum, University of Bergen
Plaited silver arm-ring B 482

Torvik, Møre og Romsdal
The Torvik hoard, 9th cent.
Historisk Museum, University of Bergen
Silver 'Hiberno-Viking' style arm-rings
and spiral rings B 7799

**Tresfjorden, Vestness, Møre og
Romsdal**
Historisk Museum, University of Bergen
Jet amulet B 290

SOGN OG FJORDANE

**Ytre Moa, Årdal, Sogn og
Fjordane**
Historisk Museum, University of Bergen
Iron strike-a-light B 11705

**Tokvam, Aurland, Sogn og
Fjordane**
Historisk Museum, University of Bergen
Female grave find
Gilt copper-alloy harness mount B 8669

**Vinjum, Aurland, Sogn og
Fjordane**
Historisk Museum, University of Bergen
Female grave find
Pair of copper-alloy oval brooches B 7731

**Tjugum, Balestrand, Sogn og
Fjordane**
Historisk Museum, University of Bergen
Clay crucible B 8025

**Myklebustad, Eid, Sogn og
Fjordane**
Historisk Museum, University of Bergen
Ship burial
Irish copper-alloy hanging bowl inlaid
with enamel B 2878

**Bø, Breim, Gloppen, Sogn og
Fjordane**
Historisk Museum, University of Bergen
Male grave find
Iron sickle B 6618

**Skrøppa, Breim, Gloppen, Sogn
og Fjordane**
Historisk Museum, University of Bergen
Grave find
Gilt copper-alloy disc with cross B 11304

Eide, Gloppen, Sogn og Fjordane
Historisk Museum, University of Bergen
Male grave
find Iron shield boss B 4611d

**Skrøppa, Breim, Gloppen, Sogn
og Fjordane**
Historisk Museum, University of Bergen
Iron leaf knife B 6577

**Sårheim, Gloppen, Sogn og
Fjordane**
Historisk Museum, University of Bergen
Silver 'thistle' brooch B 6675

**Sårheim, Gloppen, Sogn og
Fjordane**
Historisk Museum, University of Bergen
Grave find
Iron roasting fork B 6735

**Grødes, Hornindal, Sogn og
Fjordane**
Historisk Museum, University of Bergen
Female grave find
Pair of copper-alloy oval brooches
B 8000

**Vangestad, Kaupanger, Sogn og
Fjordane**
Historisk Museum, University of Bergen
Male grave find
Iron shears B 9485

Berdal, Leikanger, Sogn og Fjordane
Historisk Museum, University of Bergen
Grave find
Pair of copper-alloy oval brooches B 601

Bolstad, Luster, Sogn og Fjordane
Historisk Museum, University of Bergen
Male grave find
Iron key B 4165

Amla, Kaupanger, Sogndal, Sogn og Fjordane
Historisk Museum, University of Bergen
Ship burial
Pair of iron stirrups inlaid with brass
B 10447

Vangstad, Kaupanger, Sogndal, Sogn og Fjordane
Historisk Museum, University of Bergen
Male grave group
Iron arrowheads B 9485g
Iron axe B 9485c
Iron spearhead B 9485f
Iron sword B 9485a

Amla, Kaupanger, Sogndal, Sogn og Fjordane
Historisk Museum, University of Bergen
Iron ard B 799

Kvåle, Sogndal, Sogn og Fjordane
Historisk Museum, University of Bergen
Grave find
Iron spit B 3456

Rugeseter, Sogndal, Sogn og Fjordane
Historisk Museum, University of Bergen
Male grave group
Iron anvil B 4584s
Iron hoe B 4584
Iron pincers B 4584h
Iron scythe B 4584

Vik, Stryn, Sogn og Fjordane
Historisk Museum, University of Bergen
Male grave find
Iron tongs B 4756g

Fjellheim, Vik, Sogn og Fjordane
Historisk Museum, University of Bergen
Female grave find
Copper-alloy trefoil brooch B 8430

TROMS

Grytdy, Trondenes, Troms
Historisk Museum, University of Bergen
Ship burial
Whalebone plaque, probably used as an ironing board (replica) B 274
Weaving batten B 274

SWEDEN

SWEDEN
Kungl Myntkabinettet, Stockholm
Brass-plated iron weight KMK 100 664

GASTRIKLAND

Hemlingby, Valbo sn, Gastrikland
Statens Historiska Museum, Stockholm
Set of copper-alloy coated iron weights
SHM 19802

GOTLAND

Gotland
Statens Historiska Museum, Stockholm
Cast silver bracelet with zig-zag ornament terminating in animal heads
SHM 4170

Lilla Hammars, Lokrume sn, Gotland
Statens Historiska Museum, Stockholm
Gold finger-ring SHM 11484

Barbos, Masterby sn, Gotland
Statens Historiska Museum, Stockholm
Gold finger-ring SHM 2199

Skolbetningen, Visby, Gotland
Statens Historiska Museum, Stockholm
Gold finger-ring SHM 18816

Björke, Norrgårda, Gotland
The Bjorke hoard, 9th cent.
Statens Historiska Museum, Stockholm
Silver neck-rings, arm-rings and ingots
SHM 12328

Dinese, Eksta, Gotland
Statens Historiska Museum, Stockholm
Twisted gold arm-rings SHM 714; 915

Smiss, När sn, Gotland
Statens Historiska Museum, Stockholm
Picture-stone SHM 11521

Söderkvie, Grötlingbo sn, Gotland
Statens Historiska Museum, Stockholm
Silver 'Permian' neck-ring SHM 2483

Suderbys, Bro, Gotland
Statens Historiska Museum, Stockholm
Cast silver bracelet with zig-zag ornament terminating in animal heads
SHM 8890

Norrgårda, Hamra sn, Gotland
Statens Historiska Museum, Stockholm
Twisted and plain gold arm-ring SHM 707

Dals, Lye sn, Gotland
Statens Historiska Museum, Stockholm

Silver penannular arm-rings SHM 9163

Mästermyr, Silte sn, Gotland
Statens Historiska Museum, Stockholm
Iron punch and lead pad SHM 21592

Grausne, Stenkyrka sn, Gotland
Statens Historiska Museum, Stockholm
Silver ingot with multiple nicking
SHM 8214

Tystebols, Stenkyrka sn, Gotland
Statens Historiska Museum, Stockholm
Fake 'silver' arm-ring (copper-alloy ingot covered with sheet tin) SHM 16835

Tingstäde sn, Gotland
Statens Historiska Museum, Stockholm
Iron spearhead with silver inlay
SHM 7571.226

Sigreifs, Västerhejde sn, Gotland
Statens Historiska Museum, Stockholm
Silver ringed pin SHM 2499

Vibble, Västerhejde sn, Gotland
Statens Historiska Museum, Stockholm
Silver Gotlandic penannular brooches
SHM 107-8

Botvalde, Väte sn, Gotland
Statens Historiska Museum, Stockholm
Coiled silver wire SHM 23228

HALLAND

Slottsmöllan, Halmstad, Halland
Statens Historiska Museum, Stockholm
Silver Thor's hammer pendants SHM 1603

Alslöv, Tönnersjo sn, Halland
Statens Historiska Museum, Stockholm
Silver octagonal rod arm-ring SHM 497

ÖLAND

Alvara, Böda sn, Öland
Statens Historiska Museum, Stockholm
Silver 'Permian' spiral rings SHM 15890 1-2

Nybro, Källa sn, Öland
Statens Historiska Museum, Stockholm
Silver spiral arm-rings SHM 4791

Klinta, Koping sn, Öland
Statens Historiska Museum, Stockholm
Silver pendants: spears of Odin, a Valkyrie and a strike-a-light SHM 128-9

SKÅNE

Skåne
Statens Historiska Museum, Stockholm
Silver Thor's hammer pendant with beaked head and filigree decoration
SHM 9822.810

Krapperup, Brunnby sn, Skåne
Statens Historiska Museum, Stockholm
Silver rings and coins SHM 92

Hälsingborg, Filborna sn, Skåne
The Filborna hoard, 10th cent.
Statens Historiska Museum, Stockholm
Silver ornaments, ingots and hacksilver
SHM 7858

Grönby, Grönby sn, Skåne
Statens Historiska Museum, Stockholm
Twisted silver neck-ring SHM 2185

Lackalänga, Lackalänga sn, Skåne
Statens Historiska Museum, Stockholm
Pressed gold foil pendants with filigree
ornament SHM 431

Malmö, Skåne
Statens Historiska Museum, Stockholm
Copper-alloy die for pressing foils to
make circular brooches SHM 6969

Näsby, Tolånga sn, Skåne
Statens Historiska Museum, Stockholm
Silver arm-rings SHM 6174

SÖDERMANLAND

Sibble, Grödinge sn, Södermanland
Statens Historiska Museum, Stockholm
Silver female pendant (Valkyrie) SHM
20672

Rällinge, Lunda sn, Södermanland
Statens Historiska Museum, Stockholm
Seated copper-alloy figure of Frey
(replica) SHM 14232 (original)

Långbro, Vårdinge sn, Södermanland
Statens Historiska Museum, Stockholm
Copper-alloy balance scales with box
SHM 15115

UPPLAND

Birka, Adelsö sn, Uppland
Statens Historiska Museum, Stockholm
Grave finds
Copper-alloy cruciform mount SHM Bj
511
Copper-alloy disc brooch SHM Bj 831
Copper-alloy lozenge-shaped brooch
SHM Bj 418
Copper-alloy ringed pin SHM Bj 1007
Carolingian silver mount, re-used as a
pendant SHM Bj 550
Silver pendant rings with glass beads
SHM Bj 557
Silver snake pendant SHM Bj 844

Birka, Adelsö sn, Uppland
Statens Historiska Museum, Stockholm
Antler comb SHM 5208.751
Helmeted figure of Odin pendant
(replica) SHM 2975.117a
Iron draw-plate SHM 5208
Iron punches SHM 5208.469-70; 472

Birka, Adelsö sn, Uppland
Kungl Myntkabinettet, Stockholm
Grave find
Silver penny of 'Woden/monster' type,
minted at Hedeby

Ekhammer, Kungsangen, Uppland
Statens Historiska Museum, Stockholm
Silver helmeted figure of Odin pendant
SHM 2950.31

Kärven, Hållnäs sn, Uppland
The Karven hoard, 9th/10th cent.
Statens Historiska Museum, Stockholm
Plaited silver neck-rings SHM 26039

Barkarby, Järfälla sn, Uppland
Statens Historiska Museum, Stockholm
Iron sword with copper and silver inlay
SHM 1984.26
Iron weapon amulets SHM 21965

Sundbyberg, Uppland
Statens Historiska Museum, Stockholm
Iron neck-ring with Thor's hammer
pendants (replica) SHM 29750.215

VÄSTERGÖTLAND

Kettilstorp, Onum sn, Västergötland
Statens Historiska Museum, Stockholm
Silver spiral beads SHM 4915

DENMARK

Vaalse, Isle of Falster
The Vaalse hoard, 10th cent.
*Prehistoric Department, National
Museum of Denmark, Copenhagen*
Silver rings, ornaments, ingots and
hacksilver (including a model strike-a-
light) 3494-96; 3515-46; 8434-39

Illebølle, Isle of Langeland
The Illebolle hoard, 9th cent.
*Prehistoric Department, National
Museum of Denmark, Copenhagen*
Silver neck-ring and arm-rings

JUTLAND

Trendgaarden, Aalborg, Jutland
*Prehistoric Department, National
Museum of Denmark, Copenhagen*
Soapstone mould for a cross and a Thor's
hammer pendant C 24451

Sønderholm sogn, Hornum herred, Aalborg, Jutland
*Medieval and Later Antiquities
Department, National Museum of
Denmark, Copenhagen*
Copper-alloy Ringerike-style mount
D 4930
Copper-alloy buckle loop with Ringerike
decoration and niello inlay D 4929

Blegkilde, Jutland
*Prehistoric Department, National
Museum of Denmark, Copenhagen*
Cast silver bracelet with zig-zag
ornament terminating in animal heads
C 10016

Hørdum, Jutland
*Prehistoric Department, National
Museum of Denmark, Copenhagen*
The Hordum hoard, 9th cent.
Silver 'Hiberno-Viking' style arm-rings
C 16055-7

Orupgaard, Jutland
*Prehistoric Department, National
Museum of Denmark, Copenhagen*
Cast silver bracelet
C 14/48

BORNHOLM

Knudsker, Bornholm
*Prehistoric Department, National
Museum of Denmark, Copenhagen*
Silver Thor's hammer pendant with staves
C 5

Rømersdal, Bornholm
The Rømersdal hoard, 10th cent.
*Prehistoric Department, National
Museum of Denmark, Copenhagen*
Plaited and plain silver rings with Thor's
hammer pendants 593-601

FYN

Kaerbyholm, Asperup Parish, Fyn
The Kaerbyholm hoard, 9th cent.
*Prehistoric Department, National
Museum of Denmark, Copenhagen*
Silver 'Hiberno-Viking' style arm-rings
and spiral ring fragment C 23/66; 24/66;
1/60

Harrendrup, Odense, Fyn
*Prehistoric Department, National
Museum of Denmark, Copenhagen*
Silver annular arm-ring C 11127
Twisted silver rod neck-ring C 11126

ZEALAND

Halleby River, Zealand
Prehistoric Department, National Museum of Denmark, Copenhagen
Copper-alloy Ringerike-style cruciform mount D 2119

Lerchenborg, Zealand
Prehistoric Department, National Museum of Denmark, Copenhagen
Female grave find
Silver Carolingian equal-armed brooch C 6193

COINS

ENGLAND

CHESHIRE

The Castle Esplanade hoard, Chester, Cheshire
Deposited c.965
British Museum

Anglo-Saxon Coinage
Aethelstan, 924-39, King of England
Chester
1952-12-7-173
BMS 60
Silver penny
Aethelstan, 924-39, King of England
Aethelred, York
1952-12-7-185
BMS 164

Silver penny
Aethelstan, 924-39, King of England
Oslac, Chester
1952-12-7-172
BMS 58

Silver penny
Eadmund, 939-46, King of England
Sigeferth
1952-12-7-202
BMS 336

Silver penny
Eadred, 946-55, King of England
Crisotin
1952-12-7-10
BMS 514

Silver penny
Eadgar, 959-75, King of England
Aethe(l)red, London
1952-12-7-156
BMS 1155

Silver penny
Edward the Elder, 899-924, King of

England
1952-12-7-159

The Castle Esplanade hoard, Chester, Cheshire
Deposited c.965
Grosvenor Museum, Chester

Anglo-Saxon Coinage
Silver penny
Eadgar, 959-75, King of England
Thurmod,
Chester Syll. Vol.5 (75)

Silver penny
Eadgar, 959-75, King of England
Thurmod, Chester
Syll. Vol.5 (77)

KENT

The Gravesend hoard, Gravesend, Kent
Deposited c.871
British Museum

Anglo-Saxon Coinage
Silver penny (bent)
Burgred, 852-74, King of Mercia
Lunette type
Cenred
1840-3-14-13

LANCASHIRE

The Cuerdale hoard, Lancashire
Deposited c.905
Assheton Collection, British Museum

Anglo-Saxon Coinage
Silver penny
Aethelred, 870-89, Archbishop of Canterbury
Two line type
Elfstan
1

Silver penny
Alfred, 871-99, King of Wessex
BMC type V
Liafvald
5

Silver penny
Alfred, 871-99, King of Wessex
BMC type V
W(u)lfred
4

Silver penny
Alfred, 871-99, King of Wessex
London monogram type
Tilwine
6

Silver penny
Alfred, 871-99, King of Wessex

Ornasforda type
Bernwald,
Oxford
7

Silver penny
Alfred, 871-99, King of Wessex
Ornasforda type
Bernwald, Oxford
8

Silver penny
Edward the Elder, 899-924, King of Wessex
Two line type
Aethe(l)red
9

Silver penny
Edward the Elder, 899-924, King of Wessex
Two line type
Cuthbert
10

Silver penny
Edward the Elder, 899-924, King of Wessex
Two line type
W(u)lfard
11

Silver penny
Edward the Elder, 899-924, King of Wessex
Crowned bust type
Aethe(l)red
12

Silver penny
Edward the Elder, 899-924, King of Wessex
Crowned bust type
Cuthbert
13

Silver penny
Edward the Elder, 899-924, King of Wessex
Crowned bust type
W(u)lfard
14

Silver penny
Ceolwulf II, 874-c.880, King of Mercia
As Alfred BMC type V
Ealdw(u)lf
2

Viking Coinage of East Anglia
Silver penny
Aethelstan-Guthrum, 878-90, King of East Anglia
Two line type
Elda
3

Byzantine Coinage
Heraclius and Heraclius Constantine,
Emperor from c.613 (and son)
19

Carolingian Coinage
Silver denaro
Berengar I, 888-915, King of Italy
17

Silver denier
Louis the Child, 899-911, King of
Germany
Strasbourg
18

Silver denier
Oddo, 888-97, King of the West Franks
Angers
16

Silver denier
Oddo, 888-97, King of the West Franks
Limoges
15

Arabic Coinage
Abbasid Silver dirhem
Al-Mu'tadid billah
Madinat al-Salam
21

Silver dirhem
Al-Mu'tamid Arminiyah Bardha'ah
20

Silver dirhem fragment
Al-Mu'tasim
Contemporary imitation
22

Silver dirhem fragment
Uncertain
23

**Coins displayed in the Rosewood
Cabinet presented to William
Assheton**

Gold medal of Queen Victoria
B1

Coins from the Cuerdale hoard
Viking Coinage of Northumbria
c.895-c.905

Silver pennies
Mirabilia Fecit type
B2-8

Silver penny
Dns Ds Rex
B9

Silver pennies
Mirabilia Fecit type
B10-16

Silver pennies
Mirabilia Fecit type
B17-21

Silver penny
Siefred Cunnetti type
B22-23

Silver penny and halfpenny
Cnut, King of York
York
B24-25

Silver halfpennies
Cnut, King of York
Cunnetti type
B26-27

Silver penny
Cnut, King of York
Cunnetti type
B28-38

The Cuerdale hoard, Lancashire
Deposited c.905
British Museum

Anglo-Saxon Coinage
Silver penny
Alfred, 871-99, King of Wessex
REX DORO type
Diarwald, Canterbury
1838-7-10-350
BMC 11

Silver penny
Alfred, 871-99, King of Wessex
Winchester
1854-6-21-28
BMC 156

Silver penny
Alfred, 871-99, King of Wessex
Exeter
1838-7-10-32
BMC 79

Silver penny
Alfred, 871-99, King of Wessex
Gloucester
1838-7-10-28
BMC 80

Silver penny
Alfred, 871-99, King of Wessex
BMC type V
Lulla
1838-7-10-23
BMC 183

Silver penny
Alfred, 871-99, King of Wessex
London monogram type
London
1838-7-10-289
BMC 89

Silver penny
Alfred, 871-99, King of Wessex
London monogram type
London
1838-7-10-285

BMC 92

Silver penny
Alfred, 871-99, King of Wessex
London monogram type
London
1838-7-10-286
BMC 90

Silver penny
Alfred, 871-99, King of Wessex
REX DORO type
Diarwald, Canterbury
1838-7-10-354
BMC 15

Silver penny
Alfred, 871-99, King of Wessex
REX DORO type
1838-7-10-348
BMC 8

Silver penny
Alfred, 871-99, King of Wessex
Two line type (3 groups)
Byrnelm
1838-7-10-77
BMC 225

Silver penny
Alfred, 871-99, King of Wessex
Two line type (3 groups)
Byrnelm
1838-7-10-75
BMC 223

Silver penny
Alfred, 871-99, King of Wessex
Two line type (4 groups)
Boga
1838-7-10-67
BMC 216

Silver penny
Alfred, 871-99, King of Wessex
Two line type (4 groups)
Dialinc
1838-7-10-109
BMC 256

Silver penny
Alfred, 871-99, King of Wessex
Two line type (4 groups)
Dialinc
1838-7-10-108
BMC 257

Silver penny
Edward the Elder, 899-924, King of
Wessex
Bath
1838-7-10-452
BMC 1

Silver penny
Edward the Elder, 899-924, King of
Wessex

Building type
Cuthbert
1955-7-8-39

Silver penny
Edward the Elder, 899-924, King of
Wessex
Two line type
Aethelwulf
1838-7-10-435
BMC 7

Silver penny
Edward the Elder, 899-924, King of
Wessex
Two line type
Byrnelm
1838-7-10-437
BMC 26

Silver penny
Edward the Elder, 899-924, King of
Wessex
Two line type
Wulfard
1838-7-10-447
BMC 60

Silver penny
Edward the Elder, 899-924, King of
Wessex
Two line type
Athelstan
1838-7-10-430
BMC 4

Silver penny
Ceolnoth, 833-70, Archbishop of
Canterbury
Wunhere
1838-7-10-1082
BMC 54

Silver penny
Plegmund, 890-914, Archbishop of
Canterbury
Two line type
Hunferth
1838-7-10-1091
BMC 84

Silver penny
Plegmund, 890-914, Archbishop of
Canterbury
Two line type
Hunferth
1838-7-10-1093
BMC 81

Silver penny
Ceolwulf II, 874-c.880, King of Mercia
As Alfred BMC type V
Leofwald
1915-5-7-702

Silver penny

Ceolwulf II, 874-c.880, King of Mercia
As Alfred BMC type V
Leofwald
1838-7-10-20
BMC 403

Viking Coinage
Silver halfpenny
Halfdan
Small cross type
Regnald
1838-7-10-414
BMC 869

Silver penny
Halfdan
Two emperor type
1896-4-53

Silver penny
Viking copy
Alfred's two line type
Cuthbert
1838-7-10-159
BMC 313

Silver penny
Viking copy
Alfred's two line type
Simun
1838-7-10-225
BMC 370

Silver penny
Viking copy
London monogram type
1838-7-10-305
BMC 112

Silver penny
Viking copy
London monogram type
1896-4-4-53

Silver penny
Viking copy
Ornasforda type
Oxford
1838-7-10-337
BMC 152

Silver penny
Viking copy
Cnut/Cunnetti type
1838-7-10-1282
BMC 986

Viking Coinage of East Anglia
Silver penny
Aethelstan-Guthrum, 878-90, King of
East Anglia
Ciolwulf
1838-7-10-7
BMC 95

Silver penny
Aethelstan-Guthrum, 878-90, King of

East Anglia
Elda
1838-7-10-13
BMC 100

Silver penny
St. Edmund Memorial, c.890-905
Daegmund
1838-7-10-689
BMC 337

Silver penny
St. Edmund Memorial, c.890-905
Daegmund
1838-7-10-690
BMC 336

Silver penny
St. Edmund Memorial, c.890-905
Adelberht
1838-7-10-489
BMC 146

Silver penny
St. Edmund Memorial, c.890-905
Oudelbert
1838-7-10-819
BMC 462

Silver penny
St. Edmund Memorial, c.890-905
Oudelbert
1838-7-10-815
BMC 466

Silver penny
St. Edmund Memorial, c.895-915
Uncertain moneyer
1838-7-10-1028
BMC 664

Silver penny
St. Edmund Memorial, c.895-915
Uncertain moneyer
1838-7-10-1027
BMC 379

Silver penny
St. Edmund Memorial, c.895-915
Uncertain moneyer
1838-7-10-1015
BMC 678

Silver halfpenny
St. Edmund Memorial, c.895-915
Gilehart
1838-7-10-1034
BMC 694

Silver halfpenny
St. Edmund Memorial, c.895-915
Gilehart
1838-7-10-1033
BMC 693

Silver penny
Viking copy

Herebere, Lincoln
1838-7-10-30
BMC 83

Silver penny
Viking copy
Lincoln monogram type
1867-7-16-13a
BMC 81

Viking Coinage of Northumbria
c.895-c.905

Silver penny
Siefred, King of York
1838-7-10-1230
BMC 1026

Silver penny
Siefred, King of York
1838-7-10-1235
BMC 1031

Silver penny
Siefred, King of York
1838-7-10-1234
BMC 1030

Silver penny
Siefred/Cnut, Kings of York
1838-7-10-1244
BMC 1021

Silver penny
Siefred/Cnut, Kings of York
1838-7-10-1243
BMC 1022

Silver halfpenny
Cnut, King of York
York signature
1838-7-10-1267
BMC 912

Silver halfpenny
Cnut, King of York
York signature
1838-7-10-1266
BMC 911

Silver penny
Cnut, King of York
York signature
1838-7-10-1357
BMC 871

Silver penny
Cnut, King of York
Quentovic
1838-7-10-1423
BMS 313

Silver penny
Cnut, King of York
Quentovic
1838-7-10-1430
BMS 317

Silver penny

Cnut, King of York
York signature
1838-7-10-1354
BMC 870

Silver penny
Cnut, King of York
Cunnetti type
1935-11-17-393

Silver penny
Cnut, King of York
Cunnetti type
1935-11-17-3
ex Barnett Bequest

Silver penny
Cnut, King of York
Cunnetti type
1838-7-10-1283
BMC 962

Silver penny
Mirabilia Fecit type
1838-7-10-1413
BMC 1067

Silver penny
Mirabilia Fecit type
1838-7-10-1414
BMC 1069

Northumbrian Coinage
Silver penny
Aethelwald, d.905, Elected as King of
Northumbria
Alvaldus/DNS DS REX
1838-7-10-1422
BMC 1078

Carolingian Coinage
Silver denaro
Berengar I, 888-915, King of Italy
Milan
1838-7-10-1218

Silver denaro
Berengar I, 888-915, King of Italy
1838-7-10-1217

Silver denaro
Berengar I, 915-24, Emperor
Milan
1855-6-12-493

Silver denaro
Lambert, 892-98, King of Italy
Milan
838-7-10-1215

Silver denaro
Lambert, 892-98, King of Italy
Milan
1838-7-10-1214

Silver denier
Charles the Bald, 840-75 & 875-7,
King of the West Franks

St Denis
1838-7-10-1173
BMS 118

Silver denier
Charles the Bald, 840-75 & 875-7,
King of the West Franks
Chartres
1838-7-10-1167
BMS 149

Silver denier
Charles the Bald, 840-75 & 875-7,
King of the West Franks
Blois
1838-7-10-1161
BMS 144

Silver obol
Charles the Bald, 840-75 & 875-7,
King of the West Franks
Paris
1838-7-10-1180
BMS 116

Silver obol
Charles the Bald, 840-75 & 875-7,
King of the West Franks
Le Mans
1838-7-10-1171
BMS 134

Silver denier
Oddo, 888-97, King of the West Franks
Blois
1838,7-10,1197
BMS 224

Silver denier
Louis the Child, 899-911, King of
Germany
Strasbourg
1838-7-10-1126
BMS 268

Silver denier
Louis the Child, 899-911, King of
Germany
Constance
1838-7-10-1219
BMS 270a

Papal-Imperial Coinage
Silver denaro fragment
Benedict IV/Louis III, 901-3
Hand type
1838-7-10-1223

Scandinavian Coinage
'Hedeby' Woden/monster type
1838-7-10-1227

'Hedeby' Woden/monster type
1838-7-10-1226

Silver penny
Carolingian type
1928-1-12-151

Arabic Coinage
Abbasid
Silver dirhem
Al-Mu'tadid billah
no reg. number
BMC 386

The Cuerdale hoard, Lancashire
Deposited c.905
Liverpool Museum

Coins presented to the Royal Numismatic
Society

Viking Coinage of East Anglia
Silver Penny
St. Edmund Memorial c.890-905
1953.114.1325
Syll. Vol.29 (158)

Vikings of Northumbria c.895-905
Silver penny
Siefred Rex
1953.114.1217
Syll. Vol.29 (196)

Silver penny
Sievert Rex
1953.114.1312
Syll. Vol.29 (205)

Silver penny
Ebraice Civitas
1953.114.1133
Syll. Vol.29 (206)
Silver penny
Cnut Rex
1953.114.1195
Syll. Vol.29 (264)

Silver penny
Cnut Rex
1953.114.1196 Syll.
Vol.29 (265)

Silver penny
Cnut Rex
Quentovic
1953.114.1348
Syll. Vol.29 (409)

Carolingian Coinage
Silver denier
Louis Pious, 781-813; 814-40 King of
Aquitaine & Emperor
1953.114.1855
Syll. Vol.29 (1076)

Silver denier
Oddo,887-98, King of the West Franks
1953.114.1877
Syll. Vol.29 (1100)

Silver denaro
Berengar I, 888-915, King of Italy
1953.114.1879
Syll. Vol.29 (1106)

The Cuerdale hoard, Lancashire
Deposited c.905
Lent by Her Majesty the Queen

Viking Coinage of Northumbria
c.895-905
Silver penny
Cnut, King of York
1763

Silver penny
Cnut, King of York
1764

Silver penny
Cnut, King of York
1765

Silver penny
Cnut, King of York
1766

Silver penny
Cnut, King of York
1805

Carolingian Coinage
Silver denier Charles the Bald, 840-75 &
875-77,
King of the West Franks
Melle
1767

Arabic Coinage
Abbasid
Silver dirhem
Al-Mansur
Madinat al-Salam (Baghdad) c.754-775
1768

Silver dirhem
Madinat al-Salam (Baghdad)
c.754-775
1769

Silver dirhem
Madinat al-Salam (Baghdad)
Uncertain date
1770

Silver dirhem
Madinat al-Salam (Baghdad)
Uncertain date
1771

Silver dirhem
Al-Mutamid
Madinat Jurjan c.870-92
1772

**The Halton Moor hoard, Halton
Moor, Lancashire**
Deposited c.1025
British Museum

Anglo-Saxon Coinage
Silver penny
Cnut, 1016-35, King of England

Helmet type
Brungar,
London no reg. number
BMC 395

Silver penny
Cnut, 1016-35, King of England
Helmet type
Sumerleda, Lincoln
no reg. number
BMC 327

Silver penny
Cnut, 1016-35, King of England
Helmet type
Aethelwine, York
no reg. number
BMC 85

Silver penny
Cnut, 1016-35, King of England
Helmet type
Grim, Cambridge
no reg. number
BMC 231

LINCOLNSHIRE

**The Stamford hoard, Stamford,
Lincolnshire**
Deposited c.895
British Museum
Viking Coinage
Silver penny (pecked) Viking copy
Herebere, Lincoln
1902-10-4-1

NORFOLK

**The Morley St. Peter hoard,
Norfolk**
Deposited c.925
British Museum

Anglo-Saxon Coinage
Silver penny (pecked)
Alfred, 871-99, King of Wessex
Lunette type
Tirwald
1959-12-10-80

Silver penny
Edward the Elder, 899-924, King of
Wessex
Sigar
1959-12-10-85

Silver penny
Edward the Elder, 899-924, King of
Wessex
Sigar
1959-12-10-86

Viking Coinage of Northumbria
Silver penny
St Peter Coinage, c.905-27, Anonymous issue
Swordless type
1959-12-10-5

Silver penny
St Peter Coinage, c.905-27, Anonymous issue
Swordless type
1959-12-10-6

NORTH YORKSHIRE

The Goldsborough hoard, Goldsborough, North Yorkshire
Deposited c.920
British Museum

Anglo-Saxon Coinage
Silver 'offering penny'
Alfred, 871-99, King of Wessex
Elimo(sina) type
1859-7-26-1
BMC 159

Silver penny
Edward the Elder, 899-924, King of Wessex
Two line type
Edelgar
1859-7-26-2 BMC 41

Arabic Coinage
Abbasid

Silver dirhem
5196

Samanid
Silver dirhem
5195

Ribblehead, North Yorkshire
Yorkshire Museum

Early Anglo-Saxon Coinage
Copper styca
Wulfhere, 854-900, Archbishop of Canterbury
1985.29

Copper stycas
Aethelred II, 841-44 & 844-49, King of Northumbria
1985.29 a & b

STAFFORDSHIRE

The Beeston Tor hoard, Beeston Tor Cave, Staffordshire
Deposited c.875
British Museum

Anglo-Saxon Coinage
Silver penny
Aethelred I, 863-71, King of Wessex

Lunette type
Biarnwine
1925-2-2-19

Silver penny
Alfred, 871-99, King of Wessex
Lunette type
Bosa
1925-2-2-24

Silver penny
Burgred, 852-74, King of Mercia
Lunette type
Guthmund
1925-2-2-12

Silver penny
Burgred, 852-74, King of Mercia
Lunette type
Beagstan
1925-2-2-1

SURREY

The Croydon hoard, Old Palace, Croydon, Surrey
Deposited c.857
British Museum
Anglo-Saxon Coinage
Silver penny Alfred, 871-99, King of Wessex
Lunette type
Herebald
1915-5-7-795
Silver penny
Burgred, 852-74, King of Mercia
Lunette type
Guthere
1915-5-7-697

Silver penny
Eadmund, 855-70, King of East Anglia
Eadberht
1915-5-7-735

Carolingian Coinage
Silver denier
Louis the Pious, 781-813 & 814-40, King of Aquitaine & Emperor
Temple type
1915-5-7-331
BMS 72

Found in Croydon, Surrey
British Museum

Anglo-Saxon Coinage
Silver penny
Alfred, 871-99, King of Wessex
Two emperor type (cf. Coelwulf II)
1896-4-4-63

IRELAND

CO. DUBLIN

The Clondalkin hoard, Clondalkin, Co. Dublin
Deposited c.1065
National Museum of Ireland, Dublin

Hiberno-Norse Coinage
Silver penny Crux type c.995-1000
IA 2998

Silver penny
Crux type c.995-1000
RIA 3000

Silver penny
Crux type c.995-1000
RIA 3001
Silver penny
Crux type c.995-1000
RIA 3002

Anglo-Saxon Prototypes
Silver penny
Aethelred II, 978-1016, King of England
Crux type (ex Wood Quay)
106-1982

Silver penny
Aethelred II, 978-1016, King of England
Crux type (ex Dundalk hoard)
RIA 3002

The Co. Dublin hoard, Co. Dublin
Deposited c.935
British Museum
Viking Coinage of Northumbria
Silver penny
St Peter Coinage, c.905-27, Anonymous issue
Sword type,
York
1915-5-7-772 CO.

OFFALY

The Clonmacnoise hoard, Clonmacnoise, Co. Offaly
Deposited c.1090
National Museum of Ireland

Hiberno-Norse Coinage
Silver penny
Phase III c. 1035-60
268-1979

Silver penny
Phase III c.1035-60
269-1979

Silver penny
Phase III c. 1035-60
275-1979

Silver penny
Phase III c. 1035-60
277-1979

Anglo-Saxon Protoypes
Silver penny
Aethelred II, 978-1016, King of England
Long Cross
(Provenance unknown)
8-1948

Silver penny
Aethelred II, 978-1016, King of England
Long cross (ex Lough Lene)
26-1985

CO. WESTMEATH

The Dysart no.4 hoard, Lough Ennell, Co. Westmeath
Deposited c.910
National Museum of Ireland, Dublin

Viking Coinage of East Anglia
Silver penny
St. Edmund Memorial c.890-905
36-1982

Viking Coinage of Northumbria
Silver penny
Cunnetti type c.895-900
43-1982

Silver penny
St. Peter Coinage c.905
50-1982

Carolingian Coinage
Silver denier fragment
54-1982

Arabic Coinage
Silver dirhem fragment
Al-Muktabi c.902-7
70-1982

Silver dirhem fragment
Al-Shash (Tashkent) c.896
72-1982

The Newtownlow hoard, Kilbeggan, Co. Westmeath
Deposited c.953
National Museum of Ireland, Dublin

Anglo-Saxon Coinage
Silver penny
Aethelstan, 924-39, King of England
Chester
81-1982

Silver penny
Aethelstan, 924-39, King of England
Probably Chester
82-1982

Silver penny
Eadred, 946-55, King of England

Probably Derby
84-1982

Silver penny
Eadred, 946-55, King of England
Chester
86-1982

ISLE OF MAN

The Douglas hoard, Ballaquayle, Douglas, Isle of Man
Deposited c.970
British Museum

Anglo-Saxon Coinage
Silver penny
Aethelstan, 924-39, King of England
Langport
1895-7-1-1
BMS 125

Silver penny
Eadmund, 939-46, King of England
Sarawald
1895-7-1-17
BMS 133

Silver penny
Eadred, 946-55, King of England
Baldric
E 4277
BMS 500

Silver penny
Eadwig, 955-59, King of England
Heriger
E 4280
BMS 787

Silver penny
Eadgar, 959-75, King of England
Durand
1895-7-1-20
BMS 1110

Silver penny
Eadgar, 959-75, King of England
Aelfsige
1895-7-1-13
BMS 1186

The Kirk Michael hoard (no.2), Kirk Michael, Isle of Man Deposited c.1065
The Manx Museum and National Trust, Isle of Man

Anglo-Saxon Coinage
Silver penny
Eadmund, 939-46, King of England
Two line type
Thorstan, N.E. England
76-81/1

Silver penny

Eadgar, 959-75, King of England
Fastolf, N.E. England
76-81/2

Silver penny
Cnut, 1016-35, King of England
Short cross type
Godric, Lincoln
76-81/3

Silver penny
Harold I, 1035-40, King of England
Long cross type with fleur-de-lis
Fargrim, Stamford
76-81/5

Silver penny
Edward the Confessor, 1042-66, King of England
Radiate type
Deorsige, Hertford
76-81/4

Continental Coinage
Silver denier
Duke of Normandy
Rouen
1020-50 76-82/1

Silver denier
Duke of Normandy
Rouen
1020-50 76-82/2

Hiberno-Manx Coinage
Silver penny
Derivative of Sihtric III
Imitation long cross penny of Aethelred II
Phase II c.1020-35
76-84/1

Silver penny
Imitation long cross penny of Aethelred II
(later degenerate series)
76-84/2

Silver penny
Imitation long cross penny of Aethelred II
76-84/3

Silver penny
Imitation long cross penny of Aethelred II
76-84/4

Hiberno-Norse Coinage
Silver penny
Sihtric III
Imitation long cross penny of Aethelred II
Phase II c.1020-35
76-83/1

Silver penny
Sihtric III
Imitation long cross penny of Aethelred II
Phase III c.1035-55
76-83/2

Silver penny
Imitation long cross penny of Aethelred II
Phase III c.1035-55
76-83/3

Silver penny
Imitation long cross penny of Aethelred II
76-83/4

**The Peel Castle hoard, St.
Patrick's Isle, Isle of Man**
Deposited c.1040
The Manx Museum and National Trust

Selection of Hiberno-Norse coins
82-150/C.

SCOTLAND

HEBRIDES

The Iona Abbey hoard, Iona, Hebrides
Deposited c.986
National Museums of Scotland, Edinburgh

Anglo-Saxon Coinage
Silver penny
Aethelstan, 924-39, King of England
Mule type with rosette
Wulfstan, Chester
Syll. Vol.6 (182)

Silver penny
Aethelstan, 924-39, King of England
Mule type with rosette
Tidger, Chester
Syll. Vol.6 (180)

Silver penny
Eadmund, 939-46, King of England
Small cross type
Abunel
Syll. Vol.6 (200)

Silver penny
Eadmund, 939-46, King of England
Small cross type
Aelfred
Syll. Vol.6 (201)

Silver penny
Eadred, 946-55, King of England
Small cross type
Eferulf
Syll. Vol.6 (224)

Silver penny
Eadred, 946-55, King of England
Small cross type
Aeriger
Syll. Vol.6 (222)

Silver penny
Eadwig, 955-59, King of England
Small cross type

Aesculf
Syll. Vol.6 (320)

Silver penny
Eadwig, 955-59, King of England
Small cross type
Aesculf
Syll. Vol.6 (319)

Silver penny
Eadgar, 959-75, King of England
Small cross type
Fastolf
Syll. Vol.6 (527)

Silver penny
Eadgar, 959-75, King of England
Small cross type
Fastolf
Syll. Vol.6 (526)

Silver penny
Aethelred II, 978-1016, King of England
First hand type
Thorstan, York
Syll. Vol.6 (653)

Silver penny
Aethelred II, 978-1016, King of England
First hand type
Frostulf, York
Syll. Vol.6 (652)

Continental Coinage
Silver denier
Richard I, 943-96, Duke of Normandy
Rouen
Syll. Vol.6 (745)

Silver denier
Richard I, 943-96, Duke of Normandy
Rouen
Syll. Vol.6 (746)

Hiberno-Norse Coinage
Silver penny
Eric, 952-4, King of York
Sword type
Radulf
Syll. Vol.6 (80)

The Storr Rock hoard, Skye, Hebrides
Deposited c.935
National Museums of Scotland, Edinburgh

Anglo-Saxon Coinage
Silver penny
Edward the Elder, 899-924, King of Wessex
Cross/building type
Waltere
Syll. Vol.6 (107)

Silver penny
Edward the Elder, 899-924, King of

Wessex
Cross/building type
Waltere
Syll. Vol.6 (108)

Silver penny
Aethelstan, 924-39, King of England
Building type
Wulstig
Syll. Vol.6 (144)

Viking Coinage of Northumbria
Silver penny
Sihtric VI Ivar, 921-6, King of York
Sword type
Manamot
Syll. Vol.6 (71)

Arabic Coinage
Samanid
Silver dirhem
Isma'il ibn Ahmad
Al-Shash (Tashkent)
Syll. Vol.6 (699)

Silver dirhem
Isma'il ibn Ahmad
Al-Shash (Tashkent)
Syll. Vol.6 (698)

Silver dirhem
Nasr II ibn Ahmad
Al-Shash (Tashkent)
Syll. Vol.6 (702)

Silver dirhem
Isma'il ibn Ahmad
Samarkand
Syll. Vol.6 (707)

Carolingian Coinage
Silver denier
Cologne
Syll. Vol.6 (735)

Silver dirhem
Nasr II ibn Ahmad
Al-Shash (Tashkent)
Syll. Vol.6 (706)

ORKNEY

The Burray hoard, Orkney
Deposited c.1000
National Museums of Scotland, Edinburgh

Anglo-Saxon Coinage
Silver penny
Eadwig, 955-59, King of England
Three line type
Boia, Northampton/Southampton
Syll. Vol.6 (344)

Silver penny
Eadgar, 959-75, King of England
Small cross type

Ive
Syll. Vol.6 (465)

Silver penny
Aethelred II, 978-1016, King of England
First hand type
Uncertain mint
Syll. Vol.6 (655)

Silver penny
Aethelred II, 978-1016, King of England
First hand type
Uncertain moneyer, York
Syll. Vol.6 (654)

Silver penny
Aethelred II, 978-1016, King of England
Mule Intermediate small cross type
Goda, London
Syll. Vol.6 (663)

SWEDEN

UPPLAND

Grave find, Birka, Adelsö sn, Uppland
Kungl Myntkabinettet, Stockholm

Scandinavian coinage
Silver penny
Woden/monster type (mounted as pendant)
Hedeby
KMK

SKÅNE

The Filborna hoard, Helsingborg, Skåne
Kungl Myntkabinettet, Stockholm

Arabic Coinage
Abbasid
Silver dirhem
Al-Muqtadir billah
Madinat al-Salam (Baghdad)
c.923/4
KMK 1

Samanid
Silver dirhem
Isma'il ibn Ahmad
Al-Shash (Tashkent)
c.906/7
KMK 2

Silver dirhem
Isma'il ibn Ahmad
Al-Shash (Tashkent)
c.904/5
KMK 3

Silver dirhem
Isma'il ibn Ahmad
Al-Shash (Tashkent)

c.905/6
KMK 4

Silver dirhem
Ahmad ibn Isma'il
Samarkand
c.912/3
KMK 5

Silver dirhem
Ahmad ibn Isma'il
Al-Shash (Tashkent)
c.907/8
KMK 6

Silver dirhem
Ahmad ibn Isma'il
Al-Shash (Tashkent)
c.911/12
KMK 7

Silver dirhem
Ahmad ibn Isma'il
Al-Shash (Tashkent)
c.912/13
KMK 8

Silver dirhem
Nasr ibn Ahmad
Samarkand
c.917/18
KMK 9

Silver dirhem
Nasr ibn Ahmad
Samarkand
c.919/20
KMK 10

Silver dirhem
Nasr ibn Ahmad
Samarkand
c.933
KMK 11

Silver dirhem
Nasr ibn Ahmad
Samarkand
c.942/3
KMK 12

Silver dirhem
Nasr ibn Ahmad
Al-Shash (Tashkent)
c.929/30
KMK 13

Silver dirhem
Nuh ibn Nasr
Samarkand
c.950/1
KMK 14

Silver dirhem
Nuh ibn Nasr
Samarkand c.953/4
KMK 15

SWEDEN (GENERAL)
Kungl Myntkabinettet, Stockholm

Arabic Coinage
Abbasid Silver dirhem
Al-Mu'tadid billah
Al-Basrah
c.898/9
KMK 1

Silver dirhem
Al-Muqtadir billah
Harran
c.910/1, 920, or 930/1
KMK 2
Samanid

Silver dirhem
Isma'il ibn Ahmad,
Al-Shash (Tashkent)
c.902/3
KMK 3

Silver dirhem
Ahmad ibn Isma'il
Al-Shash (Tashkent)
c.912/3
KMK 4

Silver dirhem
Nasr ibn Ahmad
Samarkand
c.918/9
KMK 5

Silver dirhem
Nasr ibn Ahmad
Samarkand
c.928/9
KMK 6
Silver dirhem
Nasr ibn Ahmad
Samarkand
c.929/30
KMK 7

Silver dirhem
Nasr ibn Ahmad
Al-Shash (Tashkent)
c.922/3
KMK 8

Silver dirhem
Nasr ibn Ahmad
Al-Shash (Tashkent)
c.925/6
KMK 9

Silver dirhem
Nasr ibn Ahmad
Al-Shash (Tashkent)
c.930/1
KMK 10

Silver dirhem
Nasr ibn Ahmad

Al-Shash (Tashkent)
c.311/19
KMK 11

Silver dirhem
Nasr ibn Ahmad
Al-Shash (Tashkent)
c.935/6
KMK 12

Silver dirhem
Nasr ibn Ahmad
Al-Shash (Tashkent)
c.937/8
KMK 13

Silver dirhem
Nasr ibn Ahmad
Al-Shash (Tashkent)
938/9 or 940/1
KMK 14

Silver dirhem
Nuh ibn Nasr
Bukhara
c.940/1
KMK 15

Silver dirhem
Nuh ibn Nasr
Bukhara
949/50
KMK 16

Silver dirhem
Nuh ibn Nasr
Samarkand
c.951/2
KMK 17

Silver dirhem
Nuh ibn Nasr
Samarkand
c.949/50
KMK 18

Silver dirhem
Nuh ibn Nasr
Samarkand
c.949/50
KMK 19

Silver dirhem
Abd al-Malik ibn Nuh
Samarkand
c.955/6
KMK 20

Swedish Find
Grosvenor Museum, Chester

Anglo-Saxon Coinage
Silver penny
Aethelred II, 978-1016, King of England
Long cross type
Othulf, Chester
Syll. Vol.5 (139)

Silver penny
Aethelred II, 978-1016, King of England
Long cross type
Swegen, Chester
Syll. Vol.5 (143)

PROVENANCE UNKNOWN
British Museum

Anglo-Saxon Coinage
Silver penny
Edward the Elder, 899-924, King of
Wessex
Building type
Cuthbert
1935-11-17-430
ex Barnett Bequest

Viking Coinage of Northumbria
Silver penny
St Peter Coinage, c.905-27,
Anonymous issue
Sword type
ex Rich 1828
BMC 1115

Liverpool Museum

Early Anglo-Saxon Coinage
Copper styca
Aethelred II, 841-44 (c.854-858), King of
Northumbria
Alghere
1953.114.1983
Syll. Vol. 29 (55)

Copper styca
Eanred, 807-41 (c.825-c.854), King of
Northumbria
Monne
1953.114.1975
Syll. Vol. 29 (47)

Copper styca
Eanred, 807-41 (c.825-c.854), King of
Northumbria
Monne
1953.114.1977
Syll. Vol. 29 (49)

Copper styca
Eanred, 807-41 (c.825-c.854), King of
Northumbria
Hwaetred
1953.114.1972
Syll. Vol. 29 (44)

Copper styca
Eanred, 807-41 (c.825-c.854), King of
Northumbria
Monne
1953.114.1976
Syll. Vol. 29 (48)

Copper styca
Eanred, 807-41 (c.825-c.854), King of

Northumbria
Wilheah
1953.114.1982
Syll. Vol. 29 (54)

Copper styca
Eanred, 807-41 (c.825-c.854), King of
Northumbria
Eadvini
1953.114.1961
Syll. Vol. 29 (33)

Viking Coinage of Northumbria
c.895-c.905

Silver penny
Cnut, King of York
York
1953.114.1131
Syll. Vol.29 (190)

Silver penny
Cnut, King of York
York
1953.114.1132
Syll. Vol.29 (191)
(ex Cuerdale)

Silver penny
Cnut, King of York
York
1953.114.1130
Syll. Vol.29 (189)

Silver penny
Siefred, King of York
York
1953.114.1316
Syll. Vol.29 (188)

Silver penny
Siefred/Cnut, Kings of York
York
1953.114.1135
Syll. Vol.29 (192)

Grosvenor Museum, Chester

Anglo-Saxon Coinage
Silver penny
Aethelstan, 924-39, King of England
Circumscription small cross type
Tiot, Chester
Syll. Vol.5 (44)

Silver penny
Aethelred II, 978-1016, King of England
Long cross type
Othulf, Chester
Syll. Vol.5 (140)

Silver penny
Aethelred II, 978-1016, King of England
Long cross type
Swegen, Chester
Syll. Vol.5 (145)

Silver penny
Aethelred II, 978-1016, King of England
Long cross type
Oscytel
Syll. Vol.5 (138)

Silver penny
Aethelred II, 978-1016, King of England
Long cross type
Swegen, Chester
Syll. Vol.5 (144)

Silver penny
Aethelred II, 978-1016, King of England
Long cross type
Othulf, Chester
Syll. Vol.5 (142)

Silver penny
Aethelred II, 978-1016, King of England
Long cross type
Othulf, Chester
Syll. Vol.5 (141)

Silver penny
Aethelred II, 978-1016, King of England
Small cross type
Gunleof, Chester
Syll. Vol.5 (165)

Silver penny
Cnut, 1016-35, King of England
Quatrefoil type
Swegen, Chester
Syll. Vol.5 (232)

Silver penny
Cnut, 1016-35, King of England
Quatrefoil type
Gunleof, Chester
Syll. Vol.5 (208)

Silver penny
Edward the Confessor, 1042-66, King of
England
Pointed helmet type
Sweartcol, Chester
Syll. Vol.5 (341)

Silver penny
Edward the Confessor, 1042-66, King of
England
Radiate small cross type
Colbrand, Chester
Syll. Vol.5 (288)

Silver penny
Edward the Confessor, 1042-66, King of
England
Short cross type
Huscarl, Chester
Syll. Vol.5 (305)

Silver penny
Harold I, 1035-40, King of England
Fleur-de-lis type
Swarting, Chester

Syll. Vol.5 (277)

Silver penny
Harold I, 1035-40, King of England
Jewel cross type
Croc, Chester
Syll. Vol.5 (270)

PHOTOGRAPHIC CREDITS

PHOTOGRAPH	CREDIT
C. M. Dixon	*p. 2*
Rebecca Lang	*p. 4*
Rebecca Lang	*p. 10*
Ann-Mari Olsen/HMB	*p. 12*
Adam Woolfitt/SGA	*p. 13*
Ivor Edmonds/NPL	*p. 14*
Ted Spiegel/SGA	*p. 16*
SHM	*p. 17*
Statens Filmsentral, Norway	*p. 17*
Statens Filmsentral, Norway	*p. 18*
Ann-Mari Olsen/HMB	*p. 18*
Statens Filmsentral, Norway	*p. 19*
C. M. Dixon	*p. 20*
Ann-Mari Olsen/HMB	*p. 21*
Ann-Mari Olsen/HMB	*p. 21*
SHM	*p. 22*
C. M. Dixon	*p. 23*
The Manx Museum and National Trust	*p. 24*
Rebecca Lang	*p. 26*
David Flower/NMGM	*p. 26*
NMI	*p. 27*
David Flower/NMGM	*p. 28*
NMS	*p. 28*
David Flower/NMGM	*p. 29*
NMI	*p. 29*
Society of Antiquaries of London	*p. 29*
David Flower/NMGM	*p. 30*
David Flower/NMGM	*p. 32*
R. A. Philpott	*p. 33*
David Flower/NMGM	*p. 34*
Courtesy of the Trustees of the British Museum	*p. 35*
David Flower/NMGM	*p. 36*
Courtesy of the Trustees of the British Museum	*p. 38*
David Flower/NMGM	*p. 39*
David Flower/NMGM	*p. 40*
Charles W. Friend/SGA	*p. 41*
NMI	*p. 42*
David Flower/NMGM	*p. 43*
David Flower/NMGM	*p. 44*
David Flower/NMGM	*p. 44*
Courtesy of the Trustees of the British Museum	*p. 45*
Courtesy of the Trustees of the British Museum	*p. 46*
Great Scot Pictures	

PHOTOGRAPH	CREDIT
Simon Hill/YAT	*p. 48*
Simon Hill/YAT	*p. 49*
NMI	*p. 49*
NMI	*p. 50*
NMI	*p. 50*
Werner Forman Archive	*p. 51*
The Manx Museum and National Trust	*p. 52*
David Flower/NMGM	*p. 53*
R. A. Philpott	*p. 53*
Great Scot Pictures	*p. 53*
David Flower/NMGM	*p. 54*
David Flower/NMGM	*p. 55*
Courtesy of the Trustees of the British Museum	*p. 56*
Simon Warburton, Grosvenor Museum, Chester	*p. 57*
NMI	*p. 57*
C. M. Dixon	*p. 58*
Roger White	*p. 60*
David Flower/NMGM	*p. 61*
David Flower/NMGM	*p. 62*
NMI	*p. 63*
David Flower/NMGM	*p. 63*
Courtesy of the Trustees of the British Museum	*p. 64*

Abbreviations

HMB	Historisk Museum, University of Bergen
NMGM	National Museums and Galleries on Merseyside
NMI	National Museum of Ireland
NMS	National Museums of Scotland
NPL	Northern Picture Library
SGA	Susan Griggs Agency
SHM	Statens Historiska Museum, Stockholm
YAT	York Archaeological Trust

British Library Cataloguing
in Publication Data available

© Board of Trustees of the National
Museums and Galleries on Merseyside

First published in Great Britain 1990

ISBN 0 906367 41 7